Resetting Healthcare

Post-COVID-19 Pandemic

The Patient Handbook

Sanjay Prasad, MD, FACS

ISBN 978-1-7371994-0-3 (paperback)

ISBN 978-1-7371994-1-0 (ebook)

Library of Congress Control Number: 2021909142

Manufactured in the United States of America

10 9 8 7 6 5 4 3 2 1

To my parents, Jagdish and Sharan Prasad, without whose sacrifices and support this book would not be possible.

TABLE OF CONTENTS

INTRODUCTION

Remember when MRSA made headline news? Unlike other easily treatable infections, MRSA (short for methicillin-resistant Staphylococcus aureus) came right out of a sci-fi horror film. Reports described how the virulent superbug rapidly genetically mutated, deeming traditional antibiotics powerless against it. The results were painful, deep abscesses that could turn into life-threatening conditions affecting the blood, lungs, heart, bones, and joints. Patients caught MRSA in hospitals, nursing homes, and other healthcare facilities. Suddenly, these otherwise safe spaces seemed like patient danger zones.

To make matters worse, there was MRSA's nefarious twin. You could catch community-associated MRSA practically anywhere. Now healthy high school athletes during routine practice, childcare workers at schools, and those living in crowded spaces were at risk. Combined, the two MRSAs transformed healing and health settings—like hospitals and gyms—into scary places. But that was pre-pandemic.

In terms of media attention, the MRSA siblings were quickly tossed into the "who cares?" trash bin once reports emerged of a serious illness emerging from a Chinese city in late 2019. Within months, MRSA seemed downright minor compared to what was to come. (Meanwhile, it's not as if MRSA has ceased to be a serious health threat.)

As the rest of the world celebrated the New Year in 2020, Wuhan was ground zero of a troubling bug that attacked the respiratory system. While the news of the coronavirus consumed headlines across the globe, most of those living outside China witnessed the tragedy unfolding as they would any sad catastrophe, such as a massive earthquake, a destructive hurricane, or a large-scale civil unrest, taking place in a distant country.

For those of us outside Wuhan, life went on as usual, with little to distinguish the end of 2019 from the beginning of 2020. But within months, an illness that China seemed to be effectively containing within its massive borders through austere confinement measures, which seemed possible only in an authoritarian regime, began spreading to other countries. One by one, and in rapid succession, the populations of nations outside China were being infected by coronavirus, resulting in the disease the mainstream media was now officially calling COVID-19.

From Madrid to Manhattan, what was thought to be isolated to China was now on a warpath ripping through the Western World. Unprecedented lockdowns closed the borders of countries that prided themselves on democratic fundamentals like freedom of movement and put cities that were the epicenters of economic activity into immediate and aggressive sleep mode.

In the United States, the earliest cases were narrowed down to a nursing home in Seattle. This spelled early disaster for its residents because, according to the World Health Organization (WHO), people over sixty years old had a significantly higher risk of coming down with a severe case of COVID-19 than their younger counterparts. From there the cases spread throughout the tech-heavy city.

Meanwhile, on the other side of the country, another tragedy was unfolding. New York City, Europe's gateway to the United States, was hit hard by an Old World coronavirus strain that spread through untracked transmissions. The Big Apple patients with COVID-19 symptoms flooded the city's already strained ICUs, resulting in draconian lockdown measures unseen in any other part of the country.

The virus's primary transmission mode—the exchange of respiratory droplets—combined with images of crowded ICUs, body bags piled into morgues, and patients on ventilators made the virus fodder for fearful public speculation.

Those around us who looked fine could be asymptomatic carriers. And children, thought to be safe from the virus, were coming down with a new pediatric multi-organ inflammatory syndrome that shared attributes with Kawasaki disease and toxic-shock syndrome.

Treatment of those with symptoms was complicated. Many with manageable cases of coronavirus were encouraged to recover at home in order to leave hospital beds open for those in worse shape.

Multiple reasons explain why coronavirus is more virulent than other viruses like the seasonal flu. Some patients with severe COVID-19 have experienced blood clotting. The disease may also excite the immune system, causing a cytokine storm where immune cells enter the bloodstream and attack the lungs. And in the most extreme cases, mechanical ventilation and lung bypass machines, called ECMO (extracorporeal membrane oxygenation) are used. Sadly, those who were put on ECMO had a high likelihood of not surviving.

While measures to slow the disease's spread gave healthcare professionals time to develop new treatments that saved lives, what the public was waiting for was the vaccine. An unprecedented global race was underway.

Then a miracle happened. Several vaccines were developed that showed exceptional anti-COVID-19 immune responses in all participants, thanks largely to one of the world's fastest and most aggressive mass-vaccination campaigns, nicknamed Operation Warp Speed (OWS). The hope was that OWS, along with continued masking whenever possible, would bring us to herd immunity. Although there is still concern for resistant mutant strains, we appear to be finally emerging from the deadly plague. However, a recurrence of the virus in the future is a high probability and may be around for some time.

The virus affects patients directly and indirectly, short-term and-long term. For direct effects, many people who have survived severe COVID-19 have suffered lung, heart, and neurological damage, as well as mental health traumas. And some patients are at higher risk of stroke. Then there are the indirect effects. Topping this list are the long-term needs of those whose **elective surgeries** have been postponed. This category of surgery includes lifesaving procedures that, as a result of widespread lockdowns, were postponed. For those who require treatment most, this delay posed a grave threat to their long-term well-being.

Patients across the country seek solutions to meet their needs under healthcare's new normal. In the following chapters, you'll learn about a breakthrough approach to addressing patients' most pressing medical needs.

CHAPTER 1

WHAT IS ELECTIVE SURGERY?

In early 2020, news was changing as fast around the globe as ICUs were filling up in Lombardy, Madrid, and New York. Within weeks of the infection's spread outside of China, everything and everyone became suspect of transmitting coronavirus: Can I get it from riding a bike near another cyclist or just walking down the street? Does it live on the cardboard boxes I'm receiving from Amazon? Are hugs from close family members unsafe?

Seemingly overnight, words such as *social distancing* and *asymptomatic carrier* entered the common lexicon. Masks, which in countries like ours that eschewed them in the past, were now as mandatory as wearing clothes when going out. Throughout the United States, hospitals and other medical facilities were ordered to cancel or delay nonessential **elective surgeries.**

What Is Elective Surgery?

Before explaining what it is, let's differentiate elective surgery from urgent and emergency surgeries. As these names describe, they are operations performed as a result of an urgent or emergency medical condition. Simply put, emergency surgeries treat ruptures or leaks. They must be performed immediately to avoid permanent disability or death. Or they may be able to be performed as soon as the patient is medically stable. Patients who are involved in major accidents or have acute appendicitis are examples of those who would experience some kind of rupture or leak and therefore undergo emergency surgery.

Meanwhile, elective surgeries are ones that can be scheduled in advance. In this regard, many in the public consider them less important than their urgent or emergency counterparts. They associate them with nose jobs, tummy tucks, and laser hair removal. But elective doesn't necessarily mean optional. While some elective procedures are less important, such as cosmetic surgery, others treat life-threatening conditions such as cancer, clogged arteries, colon infections, diverticulitis, and brain aneurisms.

Thus to shed this class of surgery from being associated with mainly cosmetic procedures, I refer to them as **non-urgent surgeries**, rather than elective surgeries, throughout this book.

In the United States, non-urgent procedures far outweigh emergency surgeries. The emergency-to-non-urgent surgery ratio is the number of emergency surgeries per one-hundred non-urgent surgeries. Using data gathered from 2006 to 2016, in the United States, *91.4 percent of all surgeries were non-urgent.* Meanwhile, 8.6 percent of all surgeries were urgent during that period. What is the surgical bottom line?

The total annual cost of all surgery in the United States is difficult to determine for multiple reasons, primarily because surgical costs are often lumped together with medical costs.

I estimate that in 2019, all surgical costs hovered around seven hundred billion dollars. Given the importance of non-urgent surgeries and the amount spent on them, the non-urgent surgery moratorium has had a profound impact on public health and the economy as a whole.

The following are the main motives for the mortarium:

- minimize potential exposure to coronavirus;
- save on personal protective equipment (PPE) such as masks, gloves, and gowns;
- prevent the spread through loved ones and caregivers who frequently accompany patients;
- allocate healthcare workers to focus on treating coronavirus patients.

Across the United States, the moratorium on non-urgent surgery was an emergency move to contain the virus. While many speculated, no one knew the consequences of such an unprecedented decision. In fact, there was significant pushback. "Our ability to respond to patients must not be prevented by arbitrary directives," the American Hospital Association, the Federation of American Hospitals, the Association of American Medical Colleges, and the Children's Hospital Association stated in response. Surgeons and hospitals wanted the ability to triage non-urgent surgeries according to urgency. Both wanted to leave decision-making to the surgeons on a case-by-case basis.

The moratorium has affected patients seeking non-urgent surgeries forever in the following ways:

First, the pause in non-urgent surgeries created a massive nationwide backlog. Postponed surgeries were prioritized by urgency—and their numbers piled up. The inevitable worsening of conditions due to a lack of timely treatment further complicated an already desperate situation.

What is easily treatable could become life-threatening without effective medical care. A biopsy's result could mean a patient needs a mastectomy. But if the patient must wait, her breast cancer remains in her body untreated. The same goes for MRIs that are postponed. As a result, brain and other malignant tumors go undiagnosed. An ear infection neglected could spread into the brain and result in meningitis. Chest pain could mean an imminent heart attack that could have been avoided with proper preventive care ... the list of fully treatable conditions that could turn serious or deadly without expert care is endless.

Second, when patients show up for their procedures, healthcare providers must ensure that surgeons and facilities pose no threat of COVID-19 infection. This point brings up a long list of questions that need the right answers to allay patient concerns:

- Should all patients be tested for COVID-19 before their procedures?

- At what capacity is the surgical facility running, such as 100 percent or 25 percent?

- What measures (such as mandatory masks for everyone and daily facility and equipment disinfecting) will keep caregivers who arrive with patients safe? And is there a published safety policy for patients to review?

- Does the facility have stored inventory of PPE for at least thirty days or a reliable supply chain? (Avoiding a shortage of PPE was one motive behind the cancelation of non-urgent procedures.)

- Will the facility also be treating coronavirus patients?

- What is the protocol for social distancing, use of PPE, and early COVID-19 detection amongst healthcare staff? And if staff are infected, what are procedures to notify patients who may have been exposed?

Third, as much as the above protect patients' physical well-being, they serve an important psychological purpose as well. Pre-coronavirus, surgeries were rarely met with open arms. The words, "You need surgery," triggered a series of questions ranging from "What are my other options?" to "Am I going to die?" Add to that dizzying doses of news about the life-threatening hazards of hospitals due to MRSA.

Now, at the top of people's fear is that of COVID-19 infection. From obstetrics to chest pain, we've seen staggering drops in people checking into hospitals for non-coronavirus-related reasons. Patients are no longer seeking medical care for conditions that would have previously pushed them to check into a hospital or make a doctor's appointment.

In fact, there has been about a 50 percent reduction of patients seeking surgery for heart conditions and a 67 percent drop in gastric procedures; add to that the elderly and those with conditions that place them within high-risk groups such as diabetics. Allaying anxieties will motivate some reticent patients to continue with their non-urgent treatment such as biopsies and MRIs—but not all.

Fourth, fear of coronavirus may motivate patients who are allowed to schedule their surgeries to delay their procedures even longer or seek new options to avoid operations altogether. This will create a demand for alternative forms of treatment. With this opportunity there comes great danger. Patients who are borderline surgical candidates will benefit from being offered non-surgical options. But if they are not properly informed of the risks and benefits of a particular approach, they put themselves at great risk of worsening their condition.

Last, as states and cities across the United States grapple with containing the virus, we've seen a yo-yo of closing and opening of what are deemed essential and non-essential services. Cities throughout the country have reached points where they've contained the virus and opened up restaurants, gyms, and more only to see a surge in cases that pushed those same municipalities to rapidly reverse course. And health experts regularly describe the possibilities of seasonal spikes of coronavirus cases similar to how we commonly talk about cold and flu season.

With so much uncertainty surrounding non-urgent surgeries—as we've seen throughout the country, they've been allowed, restricted, and allowed again, mainly driven by ICU capacity—patients have met their doctors via FaceTime, Google Hangouts, Skype, and Zoom. These platforms have become just as commonplace as videoconferencing with our friends, family, colleagues, and clients throughout the pandemic.

Medical appointments through iPad or smartphone cannot replace in-person doctor-patient visits. Nevertheless, the pandemic pushed what was an emerging and infrequently used doctor-patient communication tool into the mainstream. Those, such as the tech averse and the elderly, who never thought they would move their face-to-face doctor's appointments online have quickly adapted. And given that federal, state, and local governments make decisions that can force healthcare providers to change course instantly, as well as the ease and convenience of videoconferencing, the platform will be a permanent part of patient care.

Non-Urgent Surgery, Version 2.0

Patients who had been advised of the need for non-urgent surgery have waited at home for weeks and, perhaps, months due to coronavirus constraints. As you've read, the moratorium has had multiple negative consequences such as the worsening conditions of already at-risk patients. But the pause has also created massive opportunity.

Essentially, non-urgent procedures have been put in a timeout on a scale never seen before. This has given healthcare professionals time to reflect on the major problems in their industry and identify strategies and solutions to address existing burdens that will persist and only worsen as a result of the pandemic, as well as new ones.

Unnecessary and overutilization of surgical services were

a persistent and enormous problem pre-pandemic. In addition to harming patients, they were a massive waste of healthcare dollars. Of 2,016 doctors from an AMA database, 64.7 percent of the physicians surveyed believed that from 15 to 30 percent of medical care was unnecessary.

In *Health in the 21st Century: Will Doctors Survive?* Dr. Contreras concludes that 29 percent of all surgeries were not necessary.

For the entire medical industry the moratorium allows the following actions that may benefit the healthcare system in general and patients in particular:

- Reassess the necessity of non-urgent surgeries
- Redetermine surgical risks and COVID-19 risks
- Explore non-surgical options
- Reevaluate costs

From tragedy springs forth innovation. The lockdown closed corporate headquarters and lit up home offices. Brick-and-mortar retailers have died and online stores have flourished. Conventions imploded and Zoom exploded.

We are at an unprecedented time in US medical history. Patients seeking their long-overdue treatments are emerging in a new healthcare landscape with options they would have never considered pre-pandemic.

As a percentage of gross domestic product, the United States spends an astronomical 17.7 percent on healthcare, by far the highest percent in the world. Considering the toll coronavirus has taken on the US economy and the health of its citizens and the large amount of the nation's dollars spent on medical care, addressing healthcare's biggest problems is the most pressing issue facing our nation today. Skillful healthcare solutions are—in no uncertain terms—vital to providing the necessary collective jolt the United States needs after months of coast-to-coast paralysis.

The pandemic reset how doctors practice and how patients receive care. Many of these developments have forced the entire healthcare industry to reevaluate its model. In other words, core aspects of medical care, like other sectors of the economy, will not revert to the pre-pandemic status quo. The national healthcare timeout has the potential to dramatically improve patients' lives—specifically, by ameliorating surgical outcomes, lowering surgical utilization rates, and lowering costs overall.

In the next chapter, you'll learn one of the biggest obstacles patients face when it comes to finding the best healthcare providers to meet their needs.

CHAPTER 2

AVOIDING THE PATIENT TRAP

You're in a Zoom meeting with your doctor when you receive the bad news, "You're going to need surgery." Depending on the severity of the operation, an endless stream of questions will run through your mind. Will I:

- catch coronavirus at the hospital?
- be in pain?
- be disabled?
- survive?
- be able to take care of loved ones who rely on me?
- need to take time off work?
- lose my job?
- have enough disability and life insurance?
- have enough insurance to cover the surgery?
- be able to cover the deductible and out-of-pocket expenses?
- need to take out a loan?

Meanwhile, your doctor is talking to you about the benefits and risks of your procedure, as well as alternatives. The high stress and anxiety you feel means you struggle focusing on the doctor's words, so they just don't register. This is unfortunate because right now you are having to make major decisions, ones that will have a big impact on your financial and physical well-being.

"Now that we're finished here, the scheduler will set up your next appointment," your doctor tells you.

You speak with the scheduler and set your surgery date. Afterwards, you call your best friend. She has questions about the Zoom meeting and what happened. But the shock of the unknown has made it difficult for you to remember what happened during the call.

At the same time, you're not overly concerned about recalling the details of your appointment. That's your doctor's job, isn't it? You'll count on your physician's guidance and recommendations and those of his or her team. After all, they have the rigorous training to ensure you will receive high quality care.

Trusting the healthcare system, however, can be a huge mistake. This is because today's medical system is wrought with inconsistencies and conflicts of interests that don't put your needs first. Wading through the options—doctors, facilities, surgery or not, and more—can overwhelm anyone. And trying to make an optimal decision may seem impossible. That is why we have developed SurgiQuality to make the decision-making process easier and more effective.

Before explaining how SurgiQuality works for you (in chapter 5), for now, we'll explore the many cracks within the current healthcare system. Too often it fails to look out for your best interests in regard to both costs you may incur and the quality of care you receive. And worst of all, it holds you prisoner in the Patient Trap.

The Patient Trap

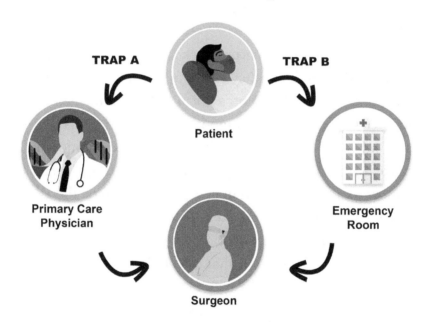

Nowadays, patients who require surgery generally fall into two categories:

A. They initially sought treatment through a primary care physician (PCP).

B. They went directly to the emergency room (ER).

Unfortunately, both patient groups wind up getting caught in the **Patient Trap** where the healthcare system captures consumers seeking medical attention. They end up having little say in who exactly cares for them or where they receive care. With little regard for their well-being, they are handed off from one provider to another, trapped in the system. By understanding how this pitfall works, you'll be able to avoid falling into it.

Patient Trap A

The patients in the first group seek medical care because they developed a condition they can cope with. Examples include a headache, a swollen joint, a burning sensation when urinating, rectal bleeding, or a lump in the throat. The patient will schedule a PCP appointment. During the consultation, PCPs make a diagnosis. If the condition is severe, they'll refer the patient to a surgeon. Herein lies the beginning of the Patient Trap. Most patients trust their PCPs with decision-making, including surgeon selection.

Little do patients know that the PCP's reason for referring one surgeon over another may not have anything to do with important measures of success. For example, surgeons may befriend PCPs on the golf course, in their houses of worship, or through their kids that are enrolled in the same schools. The following are common reasons that drive a PCP's referral decision—keep in mind that none of these has anything to do with a surgeon's cost, outcome history, and effectiveness:

- Habit over expertise

- Referral nurses

- A list of preferred specialists

- Academic referrals

- Mandatory referrals

Habit over Expertise

PCPs struggle to adhere to busy appointment schedules, oftentimes booking consecutive fifteen- and thirty-minute appointments. Within that limited time, a detailed history and focused physical examination must be performed to arrive at a diagnosis. A rational treatment plan must be formulated and articulated to the patient. Prescriptions need to be written, and the electronic medical record must be filled out as completely as possible to justify the plan.

With so many tasks packed into a half-hour or less, it's no surprise that little time remains for one of the most important steps: evaluating options and choosing the best surgical specialist for the patient's condition. With an eye on the clock, the easiest and quickest path determines the referrals, which invariably means relying upon habit. This means recommendations are usually made according to the name of the specialist on the PCP's mind and not necessarily on the area of expertise within the surgeon's specialty.

Referral Nurses

Some primary care practices may have referral nurses whose responsibility is making referrals.

A List of Preferred Specialists

PCP practices may have a short list of surgeons within each specialty. This list is seldom revised. While in and of itself, a list is not necessarily bad, the problem is when conflicts of interest that have nothing to do with improving outcomes play a role in who creates the list and who is on it.

For example, private practice and academic surgeons may aggressively lobby to gain a spot on this coveted short list. They may gift treats, accompanied by kind notes to the front office and referral nurses. They may offer free lunches and dinners to educate a PCP on the conditions they treat.

Academic Referrals

Academic institutions may organize regional meetings and seminars that have a networking and marketing component intended to promote their organizations to PCPs and surgeons. The faculty of these institutions usually conduct these gatherings where they highlight their expertise. Additionally, academic institutions may invite PCPs and surgeons to present cases at grand rounds to further strengthen ties between invited guests and faculty. At these monthly meetings, surgeons in training present interesting cases, and the faculty discuss all aspects of care, from diagnosis to treatment, citing past experience and publications. For many academic institutions, one important objective of these meetings is to strengthen ties with their physician-attendees so when patients need surgery, the physician will be motivated to directly connect with the institution's faculty members and refer his or her patients to them.

Mandatory Referrals

And the most aggressive tactic is when hospitals and academic institutions buy out PCP and surgeon practices. Once they own them, they may require referrals. All patients with certain surgical conditions are then required to be referred to the academic institution for surgical care. Hospitals and academic institutions often argue that the purpose of this mandate is to improve surgery outcomes, but undoubtedly the cost of care increases. Some may argue that increased costs incurred from having surgery at an academic institution, as opposed to in a community hospital, is justified because of improved outcomes; however, you won't find much evidence to back up this claim.

Often the PCP does not consider whether the surgeon or the facility that he or she operates is in network or out of the patient's network. And choosing the latter can be financially disastrous to the patient. In addition, the referral is not made on the basis of cost—an important consideration for those with high deductibles—or quality, which matters to every patient.

Tests a patient undergoes tend to be more expensive in a hospital setting. The facilities take advantage of this without letting patients know they can have the same tests performed elsewhere at a lower cost. For example, it is well known that nearly all patients who need surgery also require CTs, MRIs, or other diagnostic imaging. In comparison to hospital settings, freestanding radiology facilities are often a low-cost option for patients. At the same time, many hospitals have acquired freestanding radiology facilities, and this raises costs for patients. Within hospital-owned freestanding facilities, they prominently promote their organizations, including displaying their logos and triage contact numbers to encourage patients to make appointments with their surgeons, as well as offering marketing collateral about the hospitals. In fact, it seems like the marketing department is given the mandate to leave its mark wherever possible. Even the CD cases patients receive that contain their CT and MRI results serve as hospital business cards. On them, you'll find logos, triage contact numbers, and websites—all reminders of whom to call when you need surgery.

For hospitals, one major objective of these marketing efforts is to promote their facilities to a patient in the event he or she needs surgery. Unfortunately for patients who choose this path, they are often picking the expensive option over more cost-effective ones that may even have superior track records for surgical outcomes.

Patient Trap B

Patients in the second group seek medical care because they developed an acute condition—usually with a leak or rupture. They skip their PCP and go straight to the ER where they are informed their condition requires surgery. Herein lies the beginning of Patient Trap B, which has all the pitfalls of Patient Trap A, plus the following complications associated with the patient being referred to an on-call surgeon:

These surgeons agree to cover the ER in return for the privilege of being able to admit patients there and use the operating rooms. Obtaining privileges and becoming credentialed at a hospital requires a valid unrestricted state license, at the absolute minimum. Most hospitals also look at malpractice claims and adverse reports to the National Practitioner Databank. But most hospitals do not ask about quality measures related to postsurgical outcomes.

The ER coverage is rotated monthly amongst the surgeons in each specialty. In return for agreeing to be on call, surgeons "capture" patients during their rotation. The quality of the surgeon or the procedure's cost does not play a factor in the referral. In fact, on-call surgeons are more apt to operate at the referring hospital where they hold privileges because most hospitals require surgeons to have a certain number of admissions to maintain privileges.

In addition, the ER department often has an incentive to order tests such as CTs and MRIs, which can be nearly twice as expensive in the ER as at a free-standing radiology facility. Although ER personnel do not necessarily think about costs in this regard, the hospitals make CT and MRI machines easily available for the ER. Because of this convenience and a desire to practice defensive medicine, ER physicians more readily order imaging.

Upon discharge, patients usually aren't provided with medical records. Without their medical records, patients have a higher likelihood of staying where this important information resides—yet another way they are captured in the healthcare system into which they were admitted.

Whether it's Patient Trap A or B, forces are taking place behind the scenes, where unknowing patients are merely manipulated puppets in this play of who gets their money, whether from their insurance carrier or out of pocket.

Healthcare in Crisis

As if the Patient Trap wasn't enough to worry about, you must also reckon with the impact of the health insurance crisis. In 2020, the estimated median household income for a family of four was $78,500. That same year, the average family health insurance deductible was about $8,400, which is more than 14 percent of a median family's income. (An individual insurance deductible in 2020 was about $4,400.) Considering that a staggering 78 percent of Americans live paycheck to paycheck, these high deductibles often force families to make difficult financial decisions—and ones that are usually not in the best interest of their health.

Without a doubt, healthcare is in a state of emergency with consequences we've never before seen. For years, the price of healthcare costs has far outpaced the rate of inflation. In addition, worker premiums are rising in the double digits every year, and deductibles are increasing faster than wages. These unsustainable costs are leaving patients across America at a crossroads where they often must choose between their finances and their physical well-being.

Every year, more paycheck earnings are being allocated to cover healthcare and out-of-pocket costs when patients need care. In other words, American wages are being stretched thinner and thinner, which means that financial ruin due to rising healthcare costs is a reality for an alarming number of hard-working men and women. In fact, 66.5 percent of all US bankruptcies are tied to medical issues or healthcare costs.

Health savings accounts (HSAs) and flexible savings accounts (FSAs) were created to help address the burden of healthcare costs. At open enrollment, employees usually have a choice of different types of health plans, some of which may include an option for HSAs or FSAs. These accounts allow for employees to use pre-tax earnings and set them aside in a tax-deductible account to be used for medical expenses. But to qualify for an HSA, you must have a health plan with a high deductible, which is $1,400 or more for an individual or $2,800 or more for a family in 2020. There are also limits to how much you can contribute. HSA accounts can be rolled over and used the following plan year

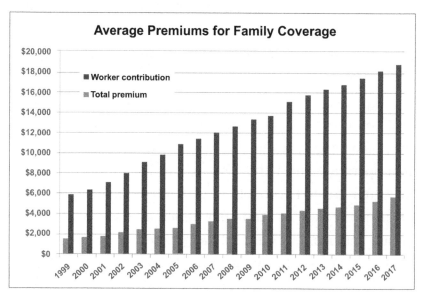

Rising health-care costs are eating up the wage gains won by American workers. Source: Kaiser Family Foundation and Heath Research & Educational Trust, Employer Health Benefits report, 2017.

An FSA, on the other hand, is available, regardless of your deductible. But it must be used in the year it was accumulated; otherwise you lose the funds.

To pay for their high deductibles, many patients who have HSAs and FSAs are dipping into them in desperation. While they are being used as a last resort, they were not designed for this purpose. Rather, they were initially developed to incent patients to shop for healthcare services. Instead of being used to satisfy the high deductibles, it would be far better for consumers if they could shop for surgical services, looking for low price and high outcomes. Also, the marketplace to shop for surgical services is in its infancy.

Last, after a serious illness or exorbitant medical bills or both, patients face the possibility of economic hardship. But, perhaps worst of all, there is another complication that can affect a patient's financial, physical, and emotional health more: unnecessary surgery.

Depending on the specialty, up to 30 percent of all surgical procedures are deemed unnecessary. Some surgeons may offer surgery as the first option, rather than considering non-operative alternatives. A torn cartilage in your knee may be better treated with physical therapy, for example, than arthroscopy surgery. And after undergoing unnecessary surgeries, patients may have recovery expenses—more costs for which they must pay and may not be able to afford. Because all surgeries carry health risks, these discretionary procedures expose their victims to morbidity, medical complications, and even death. All this is for surgery they did not need in the first place and may cause future physical harm, emotional distress, financial setback, and more.

In addition, unnecessary surgeries undermine the public's

confidence associated with them, as well as their overall faith in the healthcare system.

Next, there are the employers. To cut their ballooning healthcare costs, employers have transitioned from fully in-sured to self-insured health plans, which pass the cost burden to employees via high-deductible health plans.

The Solution

Given the Patient Trap, the health insurance state of emer-gency, and the high risk of unnecessary surgeries, now, more than ever, you need a system that places your best interests at the forefront of healthcare decisions.

SurgiQuality answers this pressing need. Rather than trust a doctor's referral without question, you have information at your fingertips: SurgiQuality provides reliable options that will help you avoid financial ruin and increase the likelihood of a positive surgical outcome. Before explaining what Surgi-Quality is, we will explore the common and widespread myths patients have when it comes to assessing surgeon quality.

CHAPTER 3

COMMON SURGEON AND MEDICAL FACILITY MYTHS

You've seen hospitals and academic institutions advertise on billboards, TV, and online, as well as on their buildings. Media coverage includes "Newsweek World's Best Hospitals," "America's Top 100 Hospitals," "Quality Award," and more.

"These must be high-quality hospitals with the best surgeons!" patients may think when they see these fancy accolades.

In our market-driven healthcare system, the most financially successful hospitals, academic institutions, and doctors have usually mastered the art of self-promotion. They spend millions building their brands through expensive online and print advertising campaigns that are long on generalizations and short on specifics. Similar to Starbucks, Toyota, and Nike, they hire prestigious and expensive advertising firms on brand identity, websites, and marketing. Their goal is to embed their names into our brains. Why else would a hospital pay for logo placement at sporting events, for example?

Then there are patient experiences. We have various subjective means, many of which are subconscious, to evaluate doctors. Meanwhile, doctors and medical facilities that are skillful self-promoters are fully conscious of these subtle forces and know how to leverage them to their benefit.

The moment patients step in the waiting room, they note its décor, size, level of activity—bustling or sleepy—and the expressions of satisfaction or anguish when other patients exit the waiting room.

When they finally meet the doctor, they will evaluate the rapport they have with him or her and the quality of the conversation. If surgeons and the offices they work for score high in all the preceding metrics, patients may perceive that a particular surgeon is of superior quality. All this is without any information about his or her skills, success rate, past patients' satisfaction, and other vital concerns.

These are just a few examples of what subjective measures patients use in their decision-making process. In the next section, you'll learn more surgeon and medical facility myths many patients believe that have little to do with what's most important: the surgeon's performance outcomes.

Myth 1: Name Brand Medical Training Means Better Outcomes

As patients wait for the surgeon in the exam room, they will scan the diplomas posted on the walls. In fact, patients may believe the names of the academic institutions are a measure of a doctor's quality. For instance, if the surgeon graduated from a well-known and prestigious medical school, this reflects his or her intelligence and training. But what you may be surprised to know is that where surgeons attended and trained has zero bearing on their surgical outcomes.

You'll be hard pressed to find any studies—let alone prestigious ones—comparing the surgical performance of graduates from top medical schools versus middle-of-the-pack or low-rated medical schools or research that shows those who graduated at the top of their classes had better surgical outcomes than the rest of their peers. And this includes whether the surgeon received his or her medical training at a domestic versus foreign medical school.

In an extensive study of 638,973 US surgeries performed by 37,221 surgeons, there was no difference between domestic and international medical graduates when looking at operative mortality, complications, and length of stay. Even when patients were stratified by severity of illness and type of procedures, no difference was found.

In addition, the number of years of medical school training required—three versus four years—has shifted back and forth. Yet there is no correlation to the skill of the surgeon based on years of training.

In the United States during World War II, the usual four-year medical school training was modified as physicians were trained in less than three years. The four-year model was again challenged in the 1970s when there was a perceived shortage of physicians. By 1973, nearly 25 percent of US medical schools offered three-year programs. They were fueled by the availability of federal capitation funding through the Comprehensive Health Manpower Training Act of 1971 (public Law 92-157). These three-year programs waned rapidly due to discontinuation of the capitation funding, declining concern about physician shortage, and faculty dissatisfaction with the pace and intensity of the programs. Students, however, were satisfied with their experiences.

Despite faculty concerns, most studies showed no significant differences in the clinical performance of the graduates of three-year and four-year programs.

Surgeons in any given specialty may seek additional expertise through an additional year of fellowship training. This is by invitation only. They are offered fellowship positions where they focus on a specific branch within their specialty and are trained by those highly respected in their field.

Generally, fellowship-trained surgeons limit their practice according to their subspecialty training. But this is not always the case. Some fellowship-trained surgeons revert to their general specialty. In addition, some surgeons have not undergone subspecialty training but may have areas of interest within their specialty that they have focused on over their careers.

Surgeons are most adept at the technologies that were present during their initial education, but some have kept pace with advancing technologies.

How is a patient to interpret and sort all these complex variables? SurgiQuality is the platform that helps patients compare surgeons using the same metrics: apples to apples and oranges to oranges. The platform goes even one step further because the metrics used are specific to the procedure they have been told they need.

Myth 2: Patients Can Rely on Online Research

With the Information Age, you'd think that surgeons and healthcare facilities would be easier to evaluate. Unfortunately, no website or application exists for patients to search for surgeons with the best skill set and surgical outcomes for their condition. And much of what you do find online provides information only about a surgeon's training, location, staff, and expertise and access to scheduling appointments.

What you won't find is procedure-specific information such as success and complication rates regarding past experiences and surgical outcomes. Unless patients take time off from work to visit other surgeons and obtain additional opinions, they will have limited access to facts and knowledge for making comparisons and an informed decision.

Without reliable and comprehensive information on surgical outcomes, success rates, and complication rates, patients are left to largely rely on anecdotal information from friends and relatives. The bottom line is nearly all patients would benefit from an advocate—an ally looking out for your best interests.

Myth 3: Awards, Ratings, Rankings, and Recognition Make a Difference

From *U.S. News & World Report*'s "Best Hospitals" to Yelp ratings, many popular awards and rankings may be persuasive, but dig deeper and their credibility often diminishes. You'll learn why in the next chapter.

Myth 4: Teaching Hospitals Are Better than Non-teaching Hospitals

Like Tesla and Apple, US academic institutions have world-wide brand recognition and prestige. This isn't just because of their naturally earned reputations. Expensive and effective marketing campaigns have resulted in the public perception that academic institutions provide better medical care than hospitals and surgery centers because they are where surgeons learn their skills and cutting-edge research happens.

In fact, according to public opinion surveys across the United States, teaching hospitals receive positive reviews and are widely seen as providing high-quality care. The *U.S. News and World Report*'s listing of America's Best Hospitals, which bases part of its ranking on the opinions of academic and community physicians, highly ranks many major teaching hospitals. But the popular report's rating methodology is problematic.

First, it is partly based on the opinions of academic and community physicians with no independent, third-party evaluating quality. Because opinions are always subject to bias, this calls into question the objectivity of the rankings themselves.

Next, self-designations such as the well-known COE (center of excellence) that hospitals and academic institutions use do not report what you think they do. (You'll learn more about these in chapter 6.) Academic institutions are guilty of reporting aggregated outcomes for all their surgeons in a given department. For instance, when it comes to cataract surgery, according to the Cleveland Clinic website, the hospital performed ten thousand procedures in 2019. But complications were tracked in only 7,139 cases. Possible reasons include inadequate follow-up in the remaining cases, deaths from other causes during the follow-up period, and tracking technology not being available. Uniform reporting standards may not have been applied. Or surgical techniques and technologies may have changed over time, making it difficult to compare groups.

One plus is that on the site, you'll find a nice breakdown on the incidence of various postoperative complications. But, just like with COE guidelines, users are unable to find information specific to their surgeons. Clearly, more transparency is needed because every procedure has its inherent complexity.

For example, what if a patient needs cataract surgery but has a previous retinal detachment or has increased eye pressure because of glaucoma? The postoperative complication rates on the Cleveland Clinic site do not provide the specific information to help those patients.

Next, academic institutions are where students are learning to be surgeons by working with patients. During a first appointment, patients will meet with the academic attending surgeon and often with any or all the following individuals: medical students, interns, residents (doctors-in-training), and fellows.

When you undergo surgery at an academic institution with a residency program, residents are involved with the operation and post-operative care. The academic attending surgeon supervises them, and inexperienced residents do not perform complex surgery. Nevertheless, before becoming a patient at an academic institution, many people fail to realize that the doctor-in-training is learning to treat patients through them.

If you want to know if medical students, interns, residents, or fellows will be involved in your care, be sure to ask because you won't be told automatically. If patients desire to have the attending surgeon perform the surgery from start to finish, they should be able to request that. But some institutions will balk at the request, reminding patients that they are in a teaching institution.

Myth 5: You Get What You Pay For: The Higher Costs of Teaching Hospitals Mean Better Outcomes

In general, costs at teaching hospitals are higher than at their non-teaching counterparts. But according to research, the results from teaching hospitals are mixed.

The most notable study related to surgery, conducted in North Carolina in 1995, found more frequent postoperative complications in teaching hospitals for stomach and intestinal operations, hysterectomy, and hip replacement compared to non-teaching hospitals.

In table 1, you'll see an analysis based on medical record reviews. In table 2, you'll see an analysis of administrative data comparing mortality rates. In both, you'll see the quality of care at some teaching hospitals was better than in their non-teaching counterparts and similar or worse in others.

Table 3.1. Studies Comparing Quality of Care in Teaching and Nonteaching Hospitals Using Medical Records as Data Source

Study	Population	Key Findings
Brennan et al. 1991	31,429 patients with all diagnoses in 51 New York City hospitals during 1984.	More frequent adverse events in major teaching hospitals than in nonteaching hospitals but less likely due to negligence.
Keeler et al. 1992	14,008 Medicare patients with congestive heart failure, acute myocardial infarction, pneumonia, stroke, or hip fracture in 297 hospitals from 5 states from 1981 to 1982 and 1985 to 1986.	Better overall process measures of quantity and lower 30-day mortality in major teaching hospitals than in nonteaching hospitals.
Zimmerman et al. 1993	15,297 patients with all diagnoses in intensive care units of 35 U.S. hospitals from 1988 to 1990.	Lower in-hospital mortality in major teaching hospitals than in other hospitals.
Pollack et al. 1994	5,451 admissions of patients with all diagnoses in national sample of pediatric intensive care units in 16 hospitals from 1989 to 1992.	Adjusted in-hospital mortality rates higher in teaching hospitals than in nonteaching hospitals.
Horbar et al. 1997	7,672 low birth weight infants in neonatal intensive care units of 62 hospitals in Vermont Oxford Network Database during 1991–92.	Similar risk of mortality within 28 days of birth in teaching and nonteaching hospitals.
Rosenthal et al. 1997	89,851 patients with myocardial infarction, congestive heart failure, pneumonia, stroke, obstructive airway disease, or gastrointestinal hemorrhage in 30 hospitals in northeast Ohio from 1991 to 1993.	Lower in-hospital mortality rates in major teaching hospitals for all study diagnoses as a group and for individual diagnoses of congestive heart failure and obstructive airway disease; similar but nonsignificant trend for acute myocardial infarction.
Ayanian et al. 1998	1,767 Medicare patients with congestive heart failure or pneumonia in 571 hospitals in Illinois, Massachusetts, New York, and Pennsylvania during 1991–92.	Better overall quality of care in major teaching hospitals than in nonteaching hospitals by process measures, particularly physicians' cognitive care and testing; similar quality of therapeutic care; worse quality of nursing care in major teaching hospitals.
Allison et al. 2000	114,411 elderly Medicare patients with acute myocardial infarction in 4,361 U.S. hospitals during 1994–95.	Greater use of aspirin, beta blockers, and ACE inhibitors and lower 30-day mortality rates in major and other teaching hospitals than in nonteaching hospitals; no difference in reperfusion therapy for ideal candidates.
Thomas, Orav, and Brennan 2000	14,700 records of patients with all diagnoses in 28 hospitals in Utah and Colorado during 1992.	Lower rates of preventable adverse drug events in government-owned major teaching hospitals than in other hospitals; similar rates of preventable adverse events in general and related to procedures or diagnoses.

Table 3.2. Studies Comparing Quality of Care in Teaching and Nonteaching Hospitals Using Medical Records as Data Source

Study	Population	Key Findings
Hartz et al. 1989	Medicare patients with all diagnoses in 3,100 U.S. hospitals during 1986.	Lower 30-day mortality rates in private teaching hospitals than in private nonteaching hospitals; no difference in mortality rates by teaching status in public hospitals.
Fleming et al. 1991	Medicare patients with all diagnoses in 657 U.S. hospitals during 1985.	Lower mortality rates in nonteaching hospitals than in teaching hospitals.
Kuhn et al. 1991	793,146 records of Medicare patients with all diagnoses in 1,219 hospitals in California, New York, Pennsylvania, Ohio, Illinois, and Texas reviewed in during 1987–88.	Fewer problems detected by peer review organizations in teaching hospitals than in nonteaching hospitals for all six states combined.
Kuhn et al. 1994	Medicare patients with all diagnoses in 3782 U.S. hospitals during 1988.	Lower mortality rates at 30 and 180 days in private, nonprofit teaching hospitals than in other hospitals.
Finkelstein et al. 1998	16,051 women in 18 Ohio hospitals for obstetrical care between 1992 and 1994.	Patients' assessments of hospital quality similar for teaching and nonteaching hospitals.
Whittle et al. 1998	22,294 Medicare patients in Pennsylvania with pneumonia during 1990.	Similar 30-day mortality rates for teaching and nonteaching hospitals; higher 90-day mortality rates for teaching hospitals.
Cunningham et al. 1999	7,901 adult patients with HIV/AIDS-related diagnoses in acute care hospitals in California during 1994.	Similar in-hospital mortality rate for teaching and nonteaching hospitals.
Peatce et al. 1999	90,331 patients with carotid endarterectomy, lower extremity bypass grafting, or abdominal aortic aneurysm repair in 835 Florida hospitals between 1992 and 1996.	Similar outcomes of hospital death, myocardial infarction, and cerebrovascular accident in teaching and nonteaching hospitals.
Schultz et al. 1999	Patients with acute myocardial infarction in 373 medical-surgical hospital in California during 1992.	Mortality lowest in limited teaching hospitals, followed by major teaching hospitals, then nonteaching hospitals.
Taylor, Whellan, and Sloan 1999	3,206 Medicare patients with hip fracture, coronary heart disease, stroke, or congestive heart failure in 1,378 U.S. hospitals between 1984 and 1994.	Lower long-term mortality rates overall and for hip fracture in major teaching hospitals than in nonteaching hospitals; similar mortality rates for stroke and congestive heart failure.
Sloan, Conover, and Provenzale 2000	32,593 patients with open or laparoscopic cholecystectomy, stomach operations, intestinal operations, hysterectomy, or hip replacement in 85 North Carolina hospitals during 1995.	More frequent postoperative complications for stomach and intestinal operations, hysterectomy, and hip replacement in teaching hospitals than in nonteaching hospitals.

Myth 6: A Surgeon's Age Should Not Play a Role in Your Healthcare Decision

When does a surgeon's age become a surgical risk factor? Considering that most surgeons graduate from medical school to begin specialty training at the age of twenty-six and that the typical surgery residency program lasts five years, this means that most surgeons begin their practice around age thirty-one. Subtract thirty-one from a surgeon's age, and you know about how long he or she has been away from medical training. For example, if your surgeon is fifty-one, she finished her medical education about twenty years before.

The timing of this initial education is also important. The technologies present at the time of a surgeon's initial education defines his or her chronological training era. In other words, surgeons who trained in a specific era are most adept with the technologies present during that timeframe. This is true for all specialties. Some surgeons keep abreast of latest technologies that develop during their career. While in and of itself this does not guarantee better patient outcomes, surgeons who stay up-to-date demonstrate a desire to continually improve and grow in their fields.

Consider orthopedic surgery, where nearly every treatment technique taught thirty-five years ago has been abandoned and replaced with more advanced procedures. Back then, all femur fractures were treated by traction for six weeks in the hospital, followed by six weeks of a plaster cast. Use of plates and screws then followed for some time.

Since the 1980s, nearly all femoral shaft fractures are treated with intermedullary nailing, surgery in which a rod or nail is permanently inserted in the center of the bone. So chances are that any orthopedic surgeon whose medical education ended by 1980 did not receive this training and had to learn the new technology on his or her own. Similarly, technological advancements have occurred in every specialty over time. Unfortunately, there has been no consistent and reliable way for patients to know if a surgeon has moved beyond the technologies that defined his or her chronological training era.

In one egregious case, a universally revered mentor of a generation of surgeons who taught at a major Midwest university hospital never really progressed from open abdominal surgery to laparoscopic abdominal surgery. Open abdominal surgery requires an incision on the abdomen, whereas laparoscopic surgery is performed through small stab incisions with visualization through endoscopes.

During one of his operations, his patient bled to death during a routine gallbladder surgery. When the hospital investigated the situation, it found that for six years, surgery schedulers were routinely ordering extra blood for possible transfusions in anticipation of his tendency to have extra-bloody operations. Investigators also found that the anesthesia department was routinely adjusting its schedule to place the most experienced anesthesiologists in this surgeon's operating room. No one ever raised a red flag.

For six years, patients were referred to this surgeon for gallbladder surgery at an academic institution. These patients were assuming they were receiving the best possible care. Tragically, these patients were receiving needless blood transfusions that carry the potential risk of transmitting hepatitis and HIV (human immunodeficiency virus). It took a death to call attention to this major oversight! This example demonstrates that patients need more transparency.

Surgeons need to maintain their current skills, develop new skills, and grow through experience. On the one hand, deterioration of purely physical skills begins near the end of a surgeon's third decade (around age twenty-eight … so yes, before one even begins to practice!). On the other hand, most surgeons reach their peak of overall performance in the second half of their fifth decade (forty-five to fifty years of age). In other words, for over twenty years, growing experience more than compensates for diminishing physical skills. But sometimes no amount of experience amassed over decades can make up for an ailing body.

My colleague Dr. Tanner described a moment early in her career when she went to see a famous neurosurgeon perform one of his renowned life-saving procedures. He was a superstar among surgeons of his specialty. Patients from around the world would pay top dollar to have him operate on them.

Like a professional musician attending the master class of a world-famous violinist, Dr. Tanner went to see the surgeon remove a tumor from the facial nerve and brain stem—a delicate procedure that required steady precision. One wrong move, and the patient's facial nerve would be damaged forever. By this time, the surgeon was seventy-nine years old, and his age showed. Viewing through an operating microscope, he used an instrument to manually dissect the tumor from the facial nerve. Dr. Tanner saw the surgeon's hand trembling in the midst of this difficult operation. She then heard him whisper to himself, "Keep still! Keep still!" admonishing his hand and coaching it into compliance.

"I couldn't believe that this doctor who was basically an idol to me was putting his patient in such danger with his shaky hand," she later told me. Unfortunately, beyond his celebrity-status, there was little other means to evaluate this famous surgeon's present skill.

An experienced surgeon will have seen many patients with different diagnoses. When a patient arrives with a rare condition, the experienced surgeon will have a better chance of recognizing the problem than the novice. Also, although the novice may learn in theory how the patient should respond to treatment, the experienced surgeon will have learned in actuality how patients respond to operations performed on them.

Generally speaking, when surgeons finish their training, they learn how to operate and when to operate. With experience, the best surgeons become more conservative and master the skill of determining when not to operate. Wisdom, experience, strength, decisiveness, and courage are required to *not* intervene. The benefit of surgery and the chance for improved quality of life must exceed the harm to a patient.

Myth 7: Upgraded and Expanding Medical Facilities Are a Measure of Successful Outcomes

You've driven by a scene like this before: Giant cranes climbing into the sky are moving massive materials, the sound of demolition and construction can be heard blocks away, and big banners flap in the wind announcing the stunning and bold new hospital wing along with the names of all the prominent community members and organizations that have contributed money to the fundraising effort. Across the country, big, beautiful hospitals or academic institutions are a source of great pride to the communities they serve.

Judging by the sleek exteriors of these new buildings, patients assume that the surgeons who operate inside are of superior quality. Patients flying in from all parts of the country and even the world for surgery only reinforces the mystique surrounding these renowned healing centers.

News stories chronicling heroic and lifesaving surgeries being performed at these facilities, such as the successful separation of Siamese twins, feeds into the notion that if surgeons at these institutions can perform the world's most complicated procedures, they can easily and skillfully perform surgeries their other patients need.

But what do these bold and big building projects have to do with surgical outcomes? In most cases, nothing. In fact, public-private partnerships through expansion of Medicaid have given some hospitals and academic institutions the money they've used to fund their physical plant expansions.

In Virginia, state legislators brokered a deal to offset hospital costs for uncompensated care through the expansion of Medicaid to families earning up to 138 percent of the federal poverty level. Under the Affordable Care Act, 90 percent of the funds for the Medicaid expansion comes from the US government, and the rest from new assessment fees on revenues from sixty-nine acute care hospitals. Medicaid will reimburse Virginia hospitals for 71 percent of an enrollee's care during the first phase of the program, rising to 88 percent soon after. Even with the extra fees, hospitals will make two dollars more in revenue for every one dollar of fees.

So what is the result of this flood of cash coming from Uncle Sam? You'll often see large crews of workers and massive cranes signaling the construction of a new hospital wing or a new façade to freshen up an outdated exterior. For instance, because of these federal-state-Medicaid expansion deals, Inova Health System, based in Fairfax, Virginia, is pushing forward with a three-hundred-million-dollar upgrade to its Loudon County hospital, and likewise, Carilion Clinic is forging ahead with a three-hundred-million-dollar expansion of Roanoke Memorial Hospital. That is, their expansions are related to securing funds from the government to serve impoverished patients and have *nothing to do* with successful patient outcomes that have resulted in greater market share. But in the realm of PR and marketing, a hospital's facelift or expansion or both are striking symbols of the hospital's exceptional role in the community.

Myth 8: Some Surgery Facilities Are Inherently Superior to Others

Surgical procedures can be divided into **outpatient** (also called ambulatory care), where patients go home the same day, and **inpatient**, where patients need time to recover in a hospital setting. Surgeons are increasingly rescheduling surgeries from inpatient to outpatient facilities. The main reasons are cost efficiency and reduced infection rate.

In the past, complicated cases were the domain of inpatient facilities. Today, however, spine fusions, disc replacements, total joint replacements, retina procedures, vaginal sling procedures, and many other higher-acuity cases have become commonplace in the outpatient setting. Some cardiovascular procedures are also migrating to ambulatory surgery centers. Hospital operating rooms are rapidly becoming the location for only the most complex procedures and higher-risk patients.

A co-morbidity is one or more diseases or conditions coexisting with another in a person. Patients with high-risk co-morbidities usually must have procedures in an inpatient setting. Examples include patients with a difficult airway where the anatomy does not allow for easy intubation, patients with fragile heart conditions, morbidly obese patients, or patients with blood-clotting abnormalities. Decisions on site of service rest solely with the surgeon and anesthesiologist.

Next, not all surgery centers are alike in terms of what they charge for surgical services. For the following section, you'll learn about different facilities and their general cost; $ indicates the lowest cost, and $$$$ indicates the highest cost:

Freestanding Ambulatory Surgery Centers (ASCs)
$
These are usually owned jointly by a surgery center management organization and the surgeons who operate there. These centers tend to be the most cost-efficient site for surgical services. The overall 0.46 percent infection rate is exceedingly low across all specialties. But in thirty-five states, ASCs are not allowed to operate without a certificate of need (CON), which is permission from the state for a healthcare facility to expand or offer a new service. Originally intended to help the poor

by providing more healthcare services to them at lower costs, CONs have done just the opposite and yet remain in place. The difficulty in obtaining a CON can vary, even in neighboring states. For example, in Virginia, freestanding ASCs find it nearly impossible to obtain a CON mainly because dominant hospital systems have a say in whether they can obtain one and in neighboring Maryland, ASCs are exempt from needing a CON as long as they have no more than one operating room. The price disparity across state lines creates a great opportunity for surgical cost savings for Virginia residents.

Hospital Outpatient Departments (HOPD) Surgery Centers $$

Hospital Outpatient Departments (HOPD) surgery centers are extensions of local hospitals and operate usually in proximity to the parent hospital. Costs for surgical services at HOPD surgery centers are nearly twice the cost of similar services at freestanding ASCs.

For example, the Medicare cost for outpatient cataract surgery at an HOPD surgery center is $1,745, compared to $976 in a freestanding ASC. Some will argue that prices at HOPDs are higher because they are forced to comply with a host of state-mandated regulations. Others say that operations in HOPD surgery centers are safer in the event an adverse event occurs. Also, the proximity to the hospital allows for the quick mobilization of resources if a patient requires it. HOPD critics argue that adverse events are extremely rare, especially when surgeons are highly selective with patient scheduling at freestanding ASCs.

The infection rate at HOPD surgery centers is 3.09 percent across all specialties, compared to 0.46 percent at freestanding ASCs. Keep in mind the percentage at HOPD surgery centers from the study cited was not adjusted according to patient acuity. In general, both pre- and post-operative patient satisfaction scores tend to be higher at surgery centers because of the smaller size of the facilities and more customized attention patients receive.

Hospitals, Hospital Systems
$$$
Academic institutions
$$$$

Hospitals are the more costly site of service for surgical procedures. According to one study, teaching hospitals have similar or less cost for surgical and non-surgical care, compared to non-teaching hospitals, when looking at Medicare reimbursements for the same procedure. But it is generally accepted that academic medical centers cost more, partly because of costs associated with graduate medical education. In 1983, Congress also established the indirect medical education (IME) payment, which partially subsidizes graduate-level medical education. IMEs and disproportionate share hospital (DSH) adjustments are additional payments for academic medical centers that serve as compensation for treating sicker patients. But both IME and DSH adjustments are shrinking every year.

Hospitals have the added burden of taking care of patients who cannot afford healthcare. In 2009, annual uncompensated care totaled $39.1 billion. In 2015 and 2016, the average nonprofit hospital spent a little more than 5 percent of its operating budget on charity care.

Costs for surgical services are higher in hospital settings, when compared to costs for similar services at surgery centers. The median costs for four procedures are as follows:

Arthroscopic knee surgery
ASC: $4,653
Hospitals: $7,061

Rotator cuff surgery
ASC: $9,290
Hospitals: $13,537

Shoulder arthroscopy
ASC: $8,819
Hospitals: $13,324

Tonsillectomy
ASC: $3,433
Hospitals: $6,944

Healthcare Mergers and Acquisitions and Patient Cost and Quality of Care

In all major US industries, mergers and acquisitions have become commonplace, and healthcare is no exception. Similar to banks, tech companies, and airlines, within the medical industry, consolidation creates opportunities for economies of scale with potential for cost reduction. These acquisitions undoubtedly have had an impact on the prices of surgical procedures and the quality of care patients receive.

In a report by the American Hospital Association, between 2009 and 2014, healthcare mergers and acquisitions
led to a cost reduction of 2.5 percent, or nearly $5.8 million.
On the flip side, consolidation also limits competition and
creates more bargaining power for healthcare organizations
to negotiate higher prices from healthcare payers. In the end,
the higher prices are borne not by the insurers but by consumers in the form of higher premiums.

When hospitals buy out surgical practices, primary care
physician practices, and diagnostic radiology facilities, they
invariably set new prices, and the new fees utilize higher
pre-negotiated fee schedules, escalating costs for consumers.
This also holds true for hospital systems and academic institutions that acquire private hospitals. Currently, there is no
convincing evidence of improvement in quality with healthcare mergers and acquisitions.

Myth 9: Malpractice Cases Are Part of the Public Domain

Out of all the malpractice lawsuits filed each year, most cases
never go to trial. Fewer than 5 percent end in a verdict, and
95 percent are settled out of court.

Confidentiality agreements in medical malpractice claims
prevent important information regarding provider quality
from entering the public domain and overall harm public
safety. In most settlements of medical negligence cases, the
defendants and their insurance companies want confidentiality. The settlement agreement specifies that the details of
the settlement, including the names of the parties and the

settlement amount, cannot be disclosed to anyone other than family members and financial advisors.

This limited access to surgeon-specific lawsuit information makes it very difficult or even impossible for patients to know if a surgeon has a history of malpractice lawsuits filed against him or her.

Conclusion

With so much information available to healthcare consumers today, knowing how to separate fact (objective and legitimate measures of quality) from fiction (subjective marketing hype and anecdotal information) is an enormous challenge. In fact, after realizing the Patient Trap exists, most patients have no idea where to even start their search for the best surgeon and medical facility.

Why is it that so many of the resources available today focus on hospitals instead of surgeons? Rather than an intentional move to make it difficult for patients to objectively measure a surgeon's performance, the reason why the public cannot do this is primarily because the technology and the infrastructure are not in place. In fact, most busy and capable surgeons fully support transparency. After all, if you're at the top of your professional game, you only have more to gain from having your expertise highlighted.

Some academic institutions are attempting to create widespread evaluation and measuring tools. But questions one must always ask when assessing the credibility of such platforms are "How objective is the information?" and "Are there conflicts of interest?" One could argue that an organization performing surgeries that is also evaluating other surgeons in competing facilities has a conflict of interest.

All these organizations are embarking down a path to promote value-based healthcare. We applaud their efforts! But what does all this mean to individual patients undergoing surgery? Unfortunately, the hospital data related to surgery is aggregated, including all surgeons in their workforce. Patients are not able to access surgeon-specific data such as past experiences with certain procedures. Where are measures such as the number of cases performed the previous year, success rates, and complication rates? How do hospitals compare surgeons within their own hospital and to surgeons in competing hospitals? In the next chapter, we'll explore common resources patients have to evaluate surgeons.

CHAPTER 4

BEWARE OF THE
HOSPITAL NEWSLETTER

L aura sits in her kitchen thumbing through a pile of mail that has grown over the last week. A warm and brightly colored newsletter from her local hospital shows up in her stack. Actually, to call it a newsletter is not quite accurate—it looks like her favorite magazine.

Her family's health is top priority, and her hospital is one of the most essential resources in her community. So rather than toss the newsletter directly in the recycle bin as she would any other piece of junk mail, she flips through it.

As Laura peruses the publication, she sees information about health and wellness, profiles of physicians, patient success stories, breakthrough treatments and technologies, stunning facility expansions, and support groups addressing conditions from autism to cancer. She finds volunteer opportunities, as well as ways to donate to its charitable foundation and a local homeless shelter.

Later in the day, she turns on the TV to see the local news. A spike in COVID-19 infection rates is the top story, and the reporter is interviewing a doctor. The physician works at her local hospital and is describing how the public can protect itself from catching the virus.

She leaves to run errands. On the way to the bank, the bus next to her has a big sign on it promoting how her city's hospital won the "Best of the Best" award. She recalls seeing a similar advertisement hanging in the basketball arena when she and her husband were watching a televised game.

Laura arrives at her bank. Unfortunately, there's a long socially distanced line. She watches a YouTube clip on her phone as she stands waiting. Her video is briefly interrupted by an advertisement. A cancer patient is being profiled. Tom is receiving life-saving treatment in the hospital's new state-of-the-art wing.

Successful healthcare facilities make quite the effort to leave their mark on a community. They are experts at epitomizing health. In fact, the country's most prestigious hospitals are perceived as modern-day temples of healing.

Laura's example demonstrates how much and effectively hospitals spend their advertising dollars. In this regard, just like a fancy Las Vegas casino, hospitals are master marketers—even extending their marketing efforts across the globe.

Unfortunately, similar to visiting anywhere in Sin City, when you're admitted to a hospital, you're also taking a big gamble. What you'll never see published in any slick marketing material is one consistent and reliable fact about hospitals in general: Once you enter, you may never leave … not quite as heart-tugging as a cancer-survivor profile in a YouTube advertisement.

Hospital-based medical errors are the third leading cause of death in the United States, behind heart disease and cancer. Some studies indicate that 250,000 to 440,000 deaths each year are attributed to medical errors in a hospital setting.

The following is a breakdown of the types of mistakes that lead to hospital deaths. There are errors of:

- **Commission:** when a mistaken action harms a patient, either because it was the wrong action or it was performed improperly. An example is the case of Representative John Murtha, who was undergoing surgical removal of the gall bladder. The surgeon accidentally perforated the intestine, resulting in a serious infection and his death.

- **Omission:** when an obvious action was necessary to heal the patient but is not performed. For example, a patient might need medication such as a beta blocker after heart surgery, and this never gets prescribed and leads to the patient's death.

- **Communication:** when communication fails between two or more providers or between a provider and a patient. An example of this is a nineteen-year-old who experienced shortness of breath when running. Having not been warned against it, he resumed jogging and three weeks later died while on a run.

- **Context:** when postoperative instructions are not adequately comprehended by the patient, even after explanation, and harm ensues.

- **Diagnosis:** when this results in a delay in treatment, no treatment, or the wrong treatment. This can happen when a pathologist mistakes healthy cells for cancer in a biopsy specimen. The patient undergoes extensive treatment, perhaps surgery, chemotherapy, and radiation treatment all for no reason. Conversely the pathologist may miss the cancer cells in the specimen, and the cancer may continue to grow and spread. Ten to 20 percent of patients may experience a diagnostic error in the United States, and forty thousand to eighty thousand patients die each year from this.

The image hospitals present to their communities can be summed up with "We're the best!" Meanwhile, in the aggregate, they are where more deaths happen than nearly any other location in the country. If this fact forms part of the definition of being the best, I shudder to think what the worst looks like.

Clearly, the branding dollars hospitals spend create results. Otherwise, they would not allocate huge amounts of money toward expensive advertising campaigns. The reward of quality marketing is the public perception of quality, and ultimately a patient scheduling a surgery in their facility. But to make the best decisions, patients require information that moves beyond the emotional and subjective. They need to be able to separate what is relevant to their needs from what is merely marketing.

Beyond hospital self-promotion, there's a lot of additional information out there. From hospital review websites to magazine rankings, the quality of the content varies widely.

Overall, patients are often left confused, overwhelmed, and uncertain about what to do. And most important, the majority of content available to patients focuses on hospitals. *But hospitals don't operate on patients, surgeon's do.* While hospitals may take credit for postoperative care, keep in mind that care is at the direction of the operating surgeon.

Surgeons are responsible for:

- what type of surgical solution to offer and when;
- the surgical approach to take;
- a patient's post-operative care.

Keep these in mind as you read the next section, which describes the common resources consumers have to decide where to have their surgeries performed.

Centers of Excellence (COE)

This is a well-known label that hospitals and academic institutions use. The COE is a self-designation, which in and of itself is huge problem because no third party is acting as a fact-checking watchdog. In fact, many awards, ratings, rankings, and designations are self-designations or based on self-reporting of data without outside oversight.

If you were looking for the best TV, would you trust the ranking Samsung gave its own products when it compared itself to the competition? Or if you were buying organic orange juice, how confident would you be if you knew the manufacturer was the only one responsible to determine its organic credibility? Self-designations often result in variables that make it difficult to compare one hospital's designation to another's.

The common way medical facilities give themselves the COE title is by treating a particular condition more than any other facility in a certain geographic area, or they have the latest robotic technology. But volume and technology do not equate to quality.

More is not the same as better—a high number of a certain procedure taking place at a facility says nothing about the quality of its outcomes. It's not the facilities themselves but ultimately the surgeons who are doing the important work. Individual surgeons are the ones who are determining when and how to operate and post-surgery patient care. Thus, when facilities publish their outcomes based on lumping all surgeons together, they are not acknowledging the importance of each doctor's performance.

For example, let's take a treatment for morbid obesity, bariatric surgery. This is the name for a category of procedures that include open or laparoscopic gastric bypass, gastric banding, and sleeve gastrectomy.

In one study of 145,527 patients treated at 165 bariatric COEs in twelve states, the risk-adjusted serious complication rate at each center varied seventeen-fold. That is, although these centers were all deemed centers for excellence, the complication rates differed tremendously. In addition, the technical skill levels varied widely for each surgeon, and that variation was strongly associated with rates of postoperative outcomes.

For the COE label to live up to its promise, it needs to reflect measures for each procedure and provide the procedure-specific outcome measures of individual surgeons, which will allow patients to make direct surgeon-to-surgeon comparisons of a doctor's experience, including the number of procedures performed the previous year and their success and complication rates. Also, all measures must be specific to a particular procedure. Last, granting the COE label must change from self-designation to coming from a third party to ensure reliable assessment of facilities. Only then will the COE designation mean the patient has the ability to make well-informed decisions.

Next, consider third-party reviews and rankings. Various organizations rate hospitals in different ways.

U.S. News & World Report is the most famous among review and ranking publications. From the best colleges and universities to hospitals, the magazine has arguably the country's best-known best-of lists. Hospitals spend big bucks adverting within the publication itself, as well as to the world, their place on the list.

The magazine ranks hospitals based on sixteen specialty areas. In twelve of these areas, ranking is determined mostly by data: cancer, cardiology and heart surgery, diabetes and endocrinology, ENT (ear, nose, and throat), gastro enterology and GI surgery, geriatrics, gynecology, nephrology, neurology and neurosurgery, orthopedics, pulmonology and lung surgery, and urology. The data used here are largely on death rates for challenging patients, on patient experience, and on other measures that are accessed using hard data. All evaluated hospitals with their results and overall scores are displayed online, but rankings are displayed only for the top fifty. For the 2019-2020 rankings, they started with 4,653 hospitals, representing virtually all US community inpatient facilities, and then narrowed their findings down.

In four specialties—ophthalmology, psychiatry, rehabilitation, and rheumatology—ranking is determined by expert opinion based on responses from three years of physician surveys. The rankings name the top fifty hospitals for complex care in each of the twelve data-driven specialties and roughly a dozen in the four expert-opinion-based specialties.

Across all sixteen specialties, only 165 US hospitals performed well enough to be nationally ranked in one or more specialties.

Hospital Compare is a consumer-oriented website, sponsored by Centers for Medicare and Medicaid Services, that provides information on how well hospitals provide recommended care to their patients. This website allows consumers to select up to three hospitals and directly compare performance-measure information related to heart attack, heart failure, pneumonia, surgery, and other conditions.

The results are organized by survey of patient experiences, timely and effective care, complications and deaths, unplanned hospital visits, psychiatric unit services, and payment and value of care. Under the complications and deaths tab and under surgical complications, users can compare three hospitals for rate of complications for hip or knee replacement, serious complications, and deaths among patients with serious treatable complications after surgery. The responses are worse than, no different than, and better than the national rate/value. Under the complications and deaths tab and under infections, users can compare hospitals based on surgical site infections from colon surgery and surgical site infections from abdominal hysterectomy. The responses are worse than, no different than, or better than the national benchmark. Under complications and deaths tab, and under 30-day death rates, users can compare hospitals for death rate after coronary artery bypass grafting surgery. The responses are worse than, no different than, or better than the national rate. In some instances, the data is not available.

This is an incredible website and a great beginning. It would benefit immensely if it also provided outcomes of hospital-specific procedures, as well as coronavirus infection rates.

Vizient is a healthcare performance improvement company helping healthcare organizations in the United States. It strengthens the delivery of high-value care and has an integrated approach to enhancing cost, quality, and market performance. Through Vizient's Clinical Data Base, which is trusted by 97 percent of academic medical centers in the United States, it provides an invaluable tool that benchmarks against peers to identify and accelerate improvements, reduce variation, and expedite data collection.

***Fortune*/IBM Watson Health 100 Top Hospitals** is a list that provides healthcare data and analytics services. Its methodology identifies fifteen top health systems through a focus on inpatient outcomes, extended outcomes, operational efficiency, and patient experience. The 100 Top Hospital and 15 Top Health System studies use publicly available databases primarily from Medicare Provider Analysis and Review (MEDPAR) and the Hospital Compare database. Their extensive analysis includes risk- and severity-adjusted algorithms.

Healthgrades methodology is slightly different from the rest. First, it determines diagnosis codes for the patient population and then considers the current condition of the patient and factors that could affect the outcome of the condition/ procedure. The methodology essentially determines existing comorbidities. Next, it determines the hospital's predicted outcome rate by summing the individual patient predicted values for each hospital. Last, using statistical tests, the methodology compares the actual outcome for each hospital with that same hospital's predicted outcome. A star rating is then assigned.

Leapfrog Group uses a Leap Frog Hospital Survey that records measures rolled up into six domains: medication safety, inpatient care management, infections, maternity care, inpatient surgery, and pediatric care. Using this website, consumers can access information on their local hospital. Pertaining to surgery, there is a tab for Problems with Surgery, and consumers can see how their hospital performs against the national average in categories such as dangerous object left in patient's body, surgical wound splits, death from serious treatable complications, collapsed lung, serious breathing problems, dangerous blood clots, and accidental cuts and tears.

Joint Council Quality Check is sponsored by the Joint Commission, an organization dedicated to becoming the gold standard for meaningful information on the performance of accredited and certified organizations to the public. The measures currently used are in the areas of immunization, palliative care, perinatal care, stroke, substance use, tobacco treatment, total hip and knee replacement, and venous thromboembolism. Certification and accreditation in the area of total hip and knee replacement is still in its infancy.

Consumer Reports provides hospital ratings based on

several categories: safety score, patient outcomes, patient experience, hospital practices, and heart surgery. The sources for data of all categories other than heart surgery are Hospital Compare and MEDPAR databases.

Under heart surgery, the following measures are used for isolated bypass surgery: patient survival, absence of surgical complications, appropriate medications, and optimal surgical technique. Measures used for successful aortic heart valve replacement include patient survival and absence of surgical complications. Congenital heart surgery measures are included separately. The sources for all heart surgery data is The Society of Thoracic Surgeons (STS).

The Society of Thoracic Surgeons has developed a national database under the categories of adult cardiac surgery, general thoracic surgery, congenital heart surgery, and Intermacs, which is a North American registry for clinical outcomes of patients who receive an FDA-approved mechanical circulatory support device to treat advanced heart failure.

Public reporting is available for three of the STS national database components: Adult Cardiac Surgery Database, Congenital Heart Surgery Database, and General Thoracic Surgery database. This too is a great start, but unfortunately, only aggregated data from groups of surgeons at each hospital are available. Furthermore, the databases are broken down into a limited number of general common procedures under each component.

Clearly this is an incredible initial effort! By STS's own admission, this is just a starting point. Patients still have to do their own research and talk with their doctors.

Conclusion

Figuring out a surgeon's proficiency for a particular procedure is difficult. In the absence of specific data, the patient may need to rely on indirect measures of proficiency. Here are some questions to consider when evaluating surgeons:

Qualifications

1. Are they board-certified in their specialty?

2. Are they a fellow of the American College of Surgeons?

3. Are they a member of specialty/sub-specialty societies related to the procedure?

Reputation

1. What are their patient satisfaction scores on consumer sites?

2. Are they on "Best Doctor" lists for community and national publications?

3. What is their malpractice history?

4. Have they ever lost their license, been suspended, or been investigated by a state medical society?

5. Are they recommended by other healthcare providers in the community?

Volume

1. How many years have they been in practice?

2. How many of these operations have they performed?

3. How many did they do in the last year?

Hospital

1. What type of facility will be used for surgery?

2. What are the resources of the hospital?

3. What is the hospital's reputation?

4. Do your other physicians have privileges at that hospital?

Outcomes

1. What outcome measures do they track?

2. What are their personal success and complication rates?

3. What are patient-reported outcomes?

SurgiQuality offers a system for patients to compare surgeons in different institutions, for procedures at varying complexity levels. This ability to compare will allow consumers to make well-informed decisions. The SurgiQuality solution helps bring out these meaningful metrics to patients contemplating surgical intervention. In the next chapter, you'll learn about this breakthrough patient resource.

CHAPTER 5

SURGIQUALITY SOLUTION

When Steve Jobs introduced the iPhone to the world in 2007, the public took notice in a flash. But no one could have ever predicted how much the modern-day device would change the world. In fact, upon its launch, some of its already popular competitors with significant market share were convinced it was just a fad that would fizzle, more toy than serious business machine. Other smartphone makers thought the lack of a physical keyboard and short battery life would never satisfy professionals' needs.

And when Elon Musk delivered Tesla's Model S to its first customers in 2012, the automaker's subsequent influence on the industry was far from certain. In fact, given the history of most car startups, failure seemed inevitable. Fast forward to today, and Tesla's success, innovation, and influence have transformed the automotive landscape.

While these examples point to companies driven by their leaders' intrinsic desire to create positive disruption on a grand scale, in other instances, external forces play a bigger role. This is especially the case with COVID-19 and the medical field.

Coronavirus has reset how doctors practice and how patients receive care. Prior to the pandemic, technology empowered citizens in multiple aspects of their lives: People looked at Trip Advisor for lodging recommendations for their family vacations. They scrolled through NextDoor to find the latest neighborhood news. And when they wanted to connect with friends, they checked Instagram. Meanwhile, when it came to their healthcare, consumer-focused online platforms lagged far behind applications that met the public's needs in other aspects of their lives.

The pandemic has pushed consumer-focused healthcare technology to the forefront of the medical industry. Just as videoconferencing went from convenience to necessity, consumer demand for practical, user-friendly, and comprehensive online healthcare solutions is greater than ever.

Furthermore, the coronavirus has put a spotlight on a patient's responsibility to take charge of his or her health conditions. Healthcare has been decidedly put in the hands of the consumer. And consumer demand is accelerating innovation.

Consumerism, according to the Institute for Healthcare Consumerism Forum, "puts economic purchasing power—and decision-making—in the hands of participants," which for our discussion, we are referring to as patients.

Throughout the lockdown, patients deferred using the healthcare system to treat their conditions by choice or force. Fear of contracting coronavirus kept patients from medical facilities. Meanwhile, lockdown measures throughout the country resulted in widespread cancellation of scheduled appointments and surgeries.

From the point of view of the consumer, one of the consequences of the pandemic on healthcare is existential. More than ever and more seriously than before, patients are asking themselves questions such as:

- Do I really need the surgery?

- Are there alternatives to surgery?

- What will be the outcomes of the surgery?

- Am I seeing the right surgeon?

- Can I afford the deductible, copay, and co-insurance? And if so, is it worth the cost?

- Can I afford the time off from work?

- Do I have enough sick leave?

- Who will take care of my loved ones?

And then there are employers. They have long favored healthcare consumerism in regard to their employees. The advent of consumer-directed healthcare accounts such as flexible spending accounts (FSAs), heath reimbursement arrangements (HRAs), and health savings accounts (HSAs) is an important initial step in this endeavor. These accounts unfortunately are being used to satisfy large deductibles in high-deductible health plans, rather than to comparison-shop healthcare services.

There is also no national competitive marketplace from where to shop today. The Free Market Medical Association, where purchasers and sellers of healthcare services can connect, is the first attempt at creating this marketplace. Here, buyers (patients and employers) can meet sellers (physicians, facilities, imaging facilities, laboratory, and preventive care providers).

Today patients in high-deductible health plans are trapped by the insurance carrier's network. In many cases, the deductible changes, depending on whether the patient seeks care from a (lower-cost) in-network or (higher-cost) out-of-network provider. Often, the deductible for one does not apply to the other. Furthermore, if the patient seeks care that the insurance carrier deems is not medically necessary, the amount paid is not applied to the deductible. Patients are so confused that they succumb to the insurance carrier's rules and stay in-network whenever possible.

But what if we could lower deductibles? Imagine having competitive pricing for the overall cost of surgical services while working with both in-network and out-of-network surgeons and facilities. And what if we could control for quality by using surgeons' measures of procedure-specific outcomes that are individually validated by surgical quality officers (experts you'll learn about in this chapter), as well as compared to other surgeons? The result is an intuitive, easy-to-understand, and powerful star grade for each surgeon. Having that level of objective and effective information for patients is unprecedented within healthcare. It signals a revolutionary win for patients and their employers!

In this chapter, you'll learn how SurgiQuality meets the needs of a healthcare landscape forever changed by coronavirus. We'll explore what SurgiQuality is, how it works, and how it offers win-win answers to today's greatest healthcare questions.

The SurgiQuality Solution

In this section you'll learn about the benefits of SurgiQuality through the experience of Sara, who suffered from intense neck pain. When patients like Sara develop a condition, they seek care from their primary care or an emergency room physician. If the condition warrants, they may be referred to a surgeon. Throughout the scenarios described in this section, the patients are already part of SurgiQuality through their employer-provided healthcare plan.

Sara was an in-house accountant who received her healthcare coverage through her employer, a small business in Bethesda. The thirty-five-year-old had developed intense neck pain that radiated down her right arm and resulted in numbness in her hand. She frequently complained of the neck pain to her husband and friends.

"I've been taking Ibuprofen for a while, but it really hasn't been helping," she told her husband, Brian.

"I really think you should go to the doctor," Brian said.

"But you know how I hate doctors," she said.

Deep down she agreed with Brian. Multiple factors. however, weighed in on her decision to grin and bear it. So instead of making the appointment, she took pain pills and watched YouTube clips about home physical therapy treatments. Some nights, she gave up tossing and turning in bed from neck pain and looked up her ailment on her iPhone. The websites told her everything from treating her condition with heat pads to surgery that fused the spine together—reading the bullet points about the risks associated with that kind of operation guaranteed another sleepless night.

Surgery scared her. But her biggest fear was cost. Sara earned sixty thousand dollars per year at her job. That amount could take her far in certain parts of the country—but even with Brian's salary, their incomes did not give them much leeway in Bethesda. In the costly Mid-Atlantic region where they lived and worked, their salaries covered living expenses but left little in savings. Far from living extravagantly, life in an expensive city just stretched their income dollars thin. Sara thought about all the stories she had heard of people going bankrupt from medical bills, and she did not want to do that to herself, let alone have insolvency affect her husband. The last thing she wanted was to wipe out their savings after major surgery.

Sara's insurance plan had a whopping ten-thousand-dollar surgery deductible. Covering this demanded more than what the couple had on hand. Although they never carried credit card balances from month to month, going under the knife would require Sara to charge part of her procedure and carry much of it forward for months with a high interest rate.

After months of her condition worsening and after Brian's and her friends' insistence, Sara finally made an appointment with her primary care doctor. He examined her and then recommended she see an orthopedic surgeon, Dr. Stuart. She had hoped her primary care physician would make a quick and easy diagnosis—but no dice. Now she was even more anxious because the unknown seemed especially worrisome.

We'll refer to Dr. Stuart as Sara's **index surgeon**, a role that distinguishes him from subsequent surgeons she may meet to evaluate and possibly treat her condition. Her other surgeons will be referred to as simply surgeons.

Dr. Stuart examined her and thought one possibility causing her pain was a herniated cervical disc putting pressure on one of the nerves that extended down her arm. He had Sara undergo an MRI. (Depending upon the conditions, surgeons may recommend blood tests, X-rays, CT scans, or other specialized tests.)

"More tests, more money, more worry," Sara thought to herself as she tried her best to stop from thinking about worst-case scenarios such as being bedridden for life in an assisted living facility or going broke or not making it out of the operating room alive.

Sara talked to Brian after meeting with Dr. Stuart.

"I'm seeing the surgeon again in a few weeks," she said.

"How do you feel about all this now?" he asked.

"To be honest, I'm getting more and more anxious with each appointment because it seems like things are getting more serious," Sara said.

"Maybe, but it's nothing for sure yet, right?" he asked.

"True, but … ," she said.

"Then there's no point in dwelling on the unknown. We're in this together; don't worry. I'll come with you to the next appointment," Brian said.

She breathed a sigh of relief. Sara had wanted to ask for help, but she was hesitant to bother even her husband. On the outside, Brian maintained calm and reassured his wife. While he refused to show any signs of fear, he too worried about her condition that now seemed more serious. Part of him wanted to tell her, "Why did you wait so long to see a doctor?" But his wiser self knew saying so would go against the unconditional support she needed right now.

"I know I'm going to have trouble focusing on whatever the doctor tells me. I may just completely zone out—or even pass out! So I really, really appreciate your help, Brian. I need your level-headedness for sure right now," she said.

During her follow-up appointment, Brian was prepared to take notes, ask important questions, and pay close attention that would ease the pressure of Sara having to bear the appointment's weight alone. Sara knew that stressful meetings like these result in information overload. The discussion would be intense and technical, and even under ideal conditions, she'd need total focus. Add the emotional component of the possibility of hearing bad news, and she knew her concentration would be affected. The three met in Dr. Stuart's exam room.

"The MRI confirmed my initial diagnosis," he said. "The herniated cervical disc is putting pressure on your nerves."

Following common protocol, Dr. Stuart provided the following information:

- The typical progression of Sara's condition if left untreated

- Surgical and non-surgical options with the risks and benefits of each

"Based on all our options, what do you recommend?" Brian asked for Sara.

"You may need to have surgery, precisely, an anterior cervical discectomy and fusion," Dr. Stuart said to Sara.

Sara and Brian collectively held their breath. They were

in shock. While they didn't know the specific type of surgery Dr. Stuart described, as a result of their prior online research, they knew the technical name meant it was a neck operation. Sara could feel her blood pressure go up. She already imagined herself on the operating table and after that, if she was lucky to come out of the hospital alive, seeing the big credit card charge on their monthly statement. What a relief that she had brought Brian with her!

Although Sara was glad she was finally receiving help for her worsening condition, the news certainly didn't provide her relief. She felt terrible for the burden her condition was putting on her husband and their marriage. She was now beating herself up for not taking action earlier. As she was processing the bad news—or *barely* processing out of shock, Brian was feverishly typing notes on his iPhone that he would later share with his wife. In fact, that evening, Sara would read those notes at home wondering if the two had been in the same meeting; she couldn't recall most of the information Brian had written down.

Brian did a great job being a third-party presence during Sara's appointment. Prior to meeting, he even went online and learned about Dr. Stuart. Brian found out about the surgeon's educational background and training. But none of that information online described anything about Dr. Stuart's surgery results and costs related to the procedures he performed, including that of the anesthesiologist and other associated expenses. While surgeons with a large cash-paying customer base may publish prices, this wasn't the case for Dr. Stuart. And during the appointment itself, like most people, neither Brian nor Sara asked key questions such as Dr. Stuart's past experience and success and complication rates—let alone how Dr. Stuart's outcomes compared to his colleagues'.

Sara and her husband's failure to seek such information is typical of patients in such cases. One reason they do not ask is that society has taught patients to confer unquestioned authority on to physicians. Another reason is patients fear offending the surgeon or sounding foolish by asking what might be considered silly questions.

A final reason is patients know surgeons are highly trained, qualified, and regulated. Thus patients have the "doctor knows best" belief that compels them to blindly or gladly defer all decisions to their surgeons, rather than ask probing questions. This belief is so perpetuated and entrenched in our society that most of us have never even been exposed to nor have any idea what relevant and fundamental questions we're supposed to ask.

In the end, under most circumstances, if Sara wanted to receive more medical opinions, she would have to first find other surgeons. This search would primarily be based on the advice of friends and family—but this is hardly an optimal evidence-based approach. Then, she would schedule appointments according to her work hours. This would require taking time off from her job and coordinating with Brian's busy schedule so he could accompany her. And given her neck pain, traveling to multiple appointments would be physically difficult.

Since Dr. Stuart had made his diagnosis and provided her options, Sara was now charged to determine how she would proceed. Neither she nor Brian was a medical professional, so the burden of this decision was overwhelming. They felt completely unqualified to figure out something that had such enormous consequences for both of them.

The great news for the couple was that Sara had a breakthrough resource to guide her through the process of finding the best surgeon for her. After her meeting with Dr. Stuart, SurgiQuality would take on her case. There are two common ways to trigger SurgiQuality's participation:

1. The patient knows he or she is already enrolled and reaches out to SurgiQuality directly.

2. The index surgeon requests authorization from the patient's insurance carrier, which knows SurgiQuality is part of the coverage. The insurance carrier then refers the case to SurgiQuality.

Sara decided to move forward with option 1 because she knew she was enrolled in SurgiQuality. Then SurgiQuality notified surgeons, beyond Dr. Stuart, of her case.

Up until now, patients, like Sara, had to rely on a hodgepodge of resources when evaluating surgeon and surgical options. From friends' opinions to questionable online content, making decisions has not been based on consistent and reliable information. SurgiQuality has forever and dramatically improved how patients make their healthcare decisions—which can be the most important ones they'll ever make in their lives. Thankfully, the old way of finding a surgeon is now obsolete.

Value to Patients

SurgiQuality provides the following values to patients:

1. Member advocacy and a personalized concierge

2. Multispecialty opinions

3. Validation of medical necessity, alternatives to surgery

4. Surgical technique differences

5. Comparison of surgeons according to past outcomes

6. Lower out-of-pocket costs

Each will be discussed in detail below.

1. Member Advocacy and a Personalized Concierge

Clearly patients need a champion who will advocate on their behalf and address their biggest concerns. Within SurgiQuality, a personalized concierge is assigned to patients, handholding them from the moment they are advised of surgery until they are back to work. The concierge strikes an extremely important and difficult balance: He or she acts as an advocate but is very careful not to steer patients toward any particular surgeon or treatment. In the end, Sara should be making well-informed decisions about her health. Having the most credible, reliable, and important information available is key to Sara's ability to decide the best approach to treat her condition.

Patients sign a HIPAA-release form, allowing the concierge access to obtain, aggregate, and distribute medical records and imaging studies. The concierge uses HIPAA-compliant communications—phone, secure messaging, and telemedicine services through SurgiQuality.

Because Sara was enrolled in SurgiQuality, she had her concierge, a healthcare expert that would take on many responsibilities that would otherwise have been left to her. She also was fortunate to have her husband's support.

By having both SurgiQuality and Brian, Sara's healthcare crisis didn't overwhelm her. She did not drown under the burden of worrying about what-if scenarios out of her control such as: What if I make a terrible decision? What if my pain doesn't go away? What if the surgery goes wrong? What if I go broke? Instead, Sara was able to focus on what she could control, specifically, the tangible steps she needed to take care of prior to surgery. These include scheduling follow-up appointments with healthcare providers and attending them, as well as obtaining blood and coronavirus tests. If she tested positive for coronavirus, she would need to follow quarantine protocols. She had many tasks to take care of, and to her relief, intense worry was no longer one of them.

In fact, rather than feeling out of control about her condition, with each SurgiQuality step, Sara gained clarity and control. She knew she had experts who were watching out for her best interests and who understood her specific needs.

SurgiQuality Customized Service

Patients can use the SurgiQuality on their smartphone to report the name of the procedure they need, desired timeframe to have the procedure, and preferred location of service and to review surgeon opinions. Alternatively, they can supply the information as they communicate with their concierge.

In Sara's case, she enlisted Brian's help. With her iPhone, he took a series of short videos that showed the mobility difference between her right and left arm. She grabbed a water bottle with each hand, and this showed how her right hand was weaker than her left. Brian also took photos of both arms to check if her right-arm muscles had atrophied. Both hoped this wasn't the case because muscle wasting is a late-stage manifestation of cervical disc disease. From her iPhone, Sara uploaded the videos and pictures to SurgiQuality.

Based on the patient's condition, he or she can provide relevant audio and video recordings. Examples include a picture of a neck mass, a video of restricted joint motion, and an audio recording of a hoarse voice or wheezing.

Eventually, SurgiQuality will use data from wearables, such as Apple Watch and devices input into clothing, to evaluate a patient's case. They provide physiological information such as blood pressure, heart rate, and temperature. Glucometer (blood sugar) readings and electrocardiographs will be imported as well. Future wearables will allow recording of pulse oximetry (blood oxygenation), electrodermal activity (electrical activity in the skin reflective of sympathetic nervous system functioning), and gait monitoring (pressure sensors in shoes for fall prevention). Not all data is relevant to a patient's case, and SurgiQuality will use only necessary information.

Upload of Medical Records and Imaging Studies
The concierge helps gather medical records, including of-

fice notes from the index surgeon's visit where he or she recommended surgery and specialized diagnostic tests. In Sara's example, this was Dr. Stuart's notes and the CD he provided her of the MRI images of her cervical spine. The concierge can obtain the DICOM (Digital Imaging and Communications in Medicine) files directly from the radiology facility. Medical records and DICOM files are uploaded to the HIPAA-compliant healthcare cloud for distribution. If Sara didn't feel comfortable uploading the information from her iPhone, she could FedEx the content to SurgiQuality.

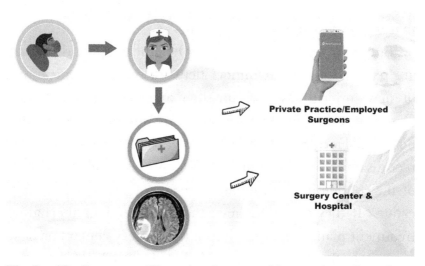

The SurgiQuality process. The patient interacts with a concierge. From there, the concierge gathers the patient's medical records and imaging. The case is then sent to surgeons, who operate at surgery centers and hospitals that are also part of the SurgiConnect network.

From the private and secure healthcare cloud, the medical records and imaging studies are sent to private practices and employed surgeons through SurgiConnect, which is the physician portal.

After verification of board certification, the profile of qualified surgeons is made active. Surgeons list surgery centers and hospitals where they have privileges to operate.

Also, surgeons indicate their specialty and areas of interest within their specialty. Many surgeons are super-specialized, honing their skills to a specific part of their specialty. For example, some neurosurgeons have focused their practice exclusively on spine surgery and no longer operate on the brain. Conversely, some neurosurgeons operate exclusively on the brain and no longer operate on the spine. Many surgeons are fellowship trained or have a certificate of added qualifications that requires extra years of training.

Surgeons and other qualified healthcare providers that are part of the SurgiConnect network receive notifications of new surgical cases within their areas of interest. Surgi-Connect is the platform for surgeons, surgery centers, and hospitals. From SurgiConnect, surgeons then review medical records and imaging, confirm the diagnosis, assess the extent of the condition, and validate necessity of the proposed procedure. If they disagree, they can recommend an alternative treatment plan. Surgeons choose the surgery centers or hospitals or both where they are privileged to safely perform the procedure.

Factors such as operating room availability, equipment, and personnel weigh into those decisions.

Surgeons and qualified healthcare providers are pinged to open the app when cases appear that are in their area(s) of interest. These are the screens for surgeons to view cases on their devices using SurgiConnect (*left to right*): welcome screen, login screen for surgeons to view patient cases, information about the patient's case, and images of the patient's case.

2. Multispecialty Opinions

SurgiQuality connects medical records of surgical patients to specialists according to their areas of interest. Different specialties share common areas of interest. The following examples are some areas of interest common to different specialties:

> **Spine:** Neurosurgeons, orthopedic surgeons, physiatrists (physical medicine and rehabilitation), acupuncture specialists, and chiropractors

> **Brain lesions:** Neurosurgeons, radiation oncologists, neurologists, and interventional radiologists

> **Colon tumors:** Colorectal surgeons, general surgeons, interventional gastroenterologists, radiation oncologists, and medical oncologists

SurgiQuality then yields opinions from different special-ists with common areas of interest, each having different points of view.

In Sara's instance, she received a range of opinions from healthcare experts that she would have otherwise not received.

Sara's case was in their area of interest, which is why they were pinged to review it. A chiropractor, neurosurgeon, or-thopedic surgeon, and physiatrist all provided their recom-mendations that reflected diverse opinions ranging from con-servative to radical. She talked to Brian and showed him the opinions on the SurgiQuality site.

"I can't believe this!" she said. "Remember how freaked out I was after my appointment with Dr. Stuart? I thought surgery was the only option. And now, I've got all these choic-es that may not require me to go under the knife. I was so bummed out before, and now I'm actually excited!"

Brian too was happy to hear the news. He was thrilled Sara had non-surgical options, and he could see the relief on her face. Plus, he was glad he had refrained from criticiz-ing her for not making a doctor's appointment earlier—some things are better left unsaid.

3. Validation of Medical Necessity, Alternatives to Surgery

After the index surgeon proposes a particular procedure (as Dr. Stuart did in Sara's example), SurgiQuality seeks new opinions. SurgiQuality asks other surgeons to evaluate that initial (in the example, Dr. Stuart's) diagnosis. If they do not agree with the index surgeon's recommendation, they can outline their rationale for an alternative plan.

Why do different surgeons in the same specialty recommend different treatment plans?

First, surgical specialists receive different training at different academic centers. Some may emphasize non-operative approaches, like acupuncture, chiropractic manipulation, or intensive physical therapy, using surgery only as a last resort.

Second, some argue that surgery has the best outcome when the condition is not as severe or when the patient is younger.

Third, surgeons initially rely on **algorithms** they learned during their medical training. You can think of these as workflows or patterns to treat specific medical issues. Imagine a patient suffers from vertigo. The algorithm would indicate when and what type of treatment, including medication, should be administered to the patient. If the condition worsens or improves, the algorithm will steer a surgeon to take a certain course of action. Surgeons have mastered algorithms and then modify them on a patient-by-patient basis based on the experience they've amassed over their careers.

Using the SurgiQuality platform, patients can learn of conservative, non-operative approaches that may prevent morbidity and even mortality. They can connect to surgeons who can customize their algorithm according to each patient's needs.

From the start, Sara was scared of surgery. While in the beginning she didn't know she had alternatives beyond what her index surgeon had recommended, Sara was excited at the prospect of treating her neck pain without an operation.

Two of the opinions she received reflected non-surgical options: The chiropractor recommended a series of appointments where she would receive chiropractic manipulation, and the physiatrist, an MD who specializes in physical medicine and rehabilitation, explained that Sara's condition might be the result of a herniated disc. This can cause inflammation around the nerve root and subsequent pain. Thus he proposed a treatment plan comprising muscle relaxants, pain and anti-inflammatory medication, heat compresses to improve blood supply, cold compresses to produce numbness, gentle stretching, muscle strengthening, home exercises, mechanical cervical traction, and steroid shots if needed.

4. Surgical Technique Differences

The **surgical approach** is the surgeon's method to gain access to the abnormality. Surgeons may differ philosophically in regard to the surgical approach for a procedure, arguing that quicker recovery or less morbidity is common with one approach versus another.

Techniques can vary in complexity, and each surgeon has his or her reason behind the recommendation.

For example, hip replacement can be performed through an anterior approach (incision in front of the hip) or posterior approach (curved incision behind the hip).

Surgeons using the anterior approach work between the muscles, pushing them aside to gain access to the hip joint. They argue that this approach offers less morbidity and quicker recovery. Not all patients, however, have the anatomy to allow for this approach.

Surgeons using the posterior approach have to cut large muscles and soft tissue to gain access to the joint. These muscles usually require repair at the end of the case. Some surgeons argue this creates more postoperative pain and longer recovery time.

Using the SurgiQuality platform, patients can learn of differences in surgical technique and ask more intelligent questions.

These are the screens for surgeons on SurgiConnect. *Left*: after surgeons have reviewed the patient's imaging and medical records, they validate the necessity of the procedure or describe an alternative treatment plan. Surgeons also input their past experience. *Middle*: private surgeons enter the surgeon's fee. Employed surgeons leave fee entry to their institution. *Right*: surgery centers and hospitals enter their fees. Keep in mind *all* fees are blinded from each other. In other words, the surgeon doesn't see facility pricing and vice-versa.

5. Comparison of Surgeons According to Past Outcomes

If you've ever sat in an exam room with a surgeon and been asked, "Do you have any questions?" you've most likely never said, "Yes, doctor. How many patients have died under your watch?" or "How many have lost a limb?" or "How many have had a stroke?" While we'd commonly label these questions as rude, the truth is they are very important.

SurgiQuality asks uncomfortable and difficult but potentially quality-of-life-improving or even life-saving questions, and surgeons answer about their past experience and outcomes with performing the procedure. In Sara's example, these questions would be tailored for cervical discectomy if that's the procedure she decides to undergo. Surgical quality officers on the SurgiQuality Quality Advisory Board formulate these questions, which are specific to a patient's procedure. They are surgeons who have held quality advisory roles in their institutions and have an interest in quality and outcomes.

The questions address the number of cases the surgeon performed the previous year (for rarer cases, this might be two or five years), as well as success, complications, and mortality rates. All surgeries are different, so based on the procedure, the outcome criteria will vary. This level of customization is essential to providing patients the most relevant and reliable information about their proposed surgery. This is why SurgiQuality has placed a priority on outcome measures, which show a doctor's surgical success rate through a star grade. SurgiQuality tailors outcome measures to each procedure, and this key feature is one of the application's most breakthrough innovations.

For example, for cataract surgery, the statistics surgeons provide are the following:

- Number of cases performed the previous year

- Percentage of patients that experienced vision better than 20/40 at ninety days postoperatively

- Percentage of patients that experienced complications within thirty days, including retinal detachment, elevated intra-ocular pressure, or infection

In Sara's instance, her questions addressed risks associated with laryngeal nerve injury (hoarseness or swallowing trouble), carotid or vertebral artery injury (stroke or death), esophageal injury (this may require high-risk esophageal surgery that can result in death), and spinal fluid leakage. Sara now had more information to perform a cost-benefit analysis of surgery versus non-surgical treatment.

Self-reported quality measures from surgeons are corroborated against queries from their individual electronic medical records. These corroborated measures are then compared to measures from all reporting surgeons for the case and, whenever possible, to the best-available national data.

Using these comparisons, each measure is assigned a one-to-five-star grade. These star grades appear on the SurgiQuality site. Now patients can compare surgeon outcome measures through star grades for the procedure they seek.

6. Lower Out-of-Pocket Costs

Private practice surgeons enter their fee to perform the procedure. Employed surgeons leave fee entry to the hospital where they are employed. Meanwhile, the chosen facility is responsible to enter the facility and anesthesia fees.

Distribution to Surgery Centers and Hospitals

Whether the patient contacts SurgiQuality directly or the insurer refers the patient's case, SurgiQuality will then notify surgeons. While surgeons are receiving notifications of the surgical case, depending on the profile specialties they serve, clinical administrators at surgery centers and hospitals are receiving the same notifications. The clinical administrators may then recommend their surgeons who are qualified to perform the procedure, and these doctors will go through the same SurgiConnect evaluation process as the other surgeons you've read about. In addition, the financial administrators at the facilities can also enter facility and anesthesia fees.

Some surgery centers and hospitals have formed all-inclusive fixed-price bundles with their surgeons for certain procedures. These bundles include the surgeon, anesthesia, and facility fees. They may also include pathology services and post-operative care. Some may offer a limited guarantee for ninety days postoperatively.

The SurgiConnect platform is versatile, working with private practice surgeons, employed surgeons, surgery centers, hospitals, hospital systems, anesthesiologists, and surgical pathologists. As we obtain pricing information from various surgeon/surgery center and surgeon/hospital combinations, an array of pricing develops. Using this pricing method, third-party administrators or health plan administrators are able to reduce or allow zero-dollar patient deductibles, co-pays, and co-insurance and at the same time control for quality. Patients can be offered financial incentives to use options with a lower cost and that achieve optimal outcomes.

Index Surgeon

In Sara's scenario, Dr. Stuart, her index surgeon, made the diagnosis and recommended surgery. Afterwards, she used SurgiQuality as a means to execute her right to choose her surgeon based on metrics she cared about most. What if, after this process, she wanted to continue with Dr. Stuart?

He is also free to join the SurgiConnect network. Dr. Stuart will enter his experience and either enter pricing or leave pricing to his facility. Because of the initial doctor-patient encounter, index surgeons have a major advantage over other doctors, having created a bond. Thus some patients will be more apt to choose that surgeon.

Procedure-Specific Quality Metrics

The following is the SurgiQuality grading system Sara received for her ACDF (anterior cervical discectomy and fusion). The more stars, the better the surgeon.

	Surgeon A	Surgeon B	Surgeon C	Surgeon D
Procedure	ACDF	ACDF	ACDF	ACDF
Necessity?	Indicated	Indicated	Indicated	Indicated
# of Cases 2019	Would Not Report	✳✳✳✳	✳	✳✳✳✳✳
Laryngeal nerve injury (hoarseness/swallowing trouble)	Would Not Report	✳✳✳✳✳	✳✳✳	✳
Carotid or vertebral artery injury (stroke/death)	Would Not Report	✳✳✳✳✳	✳✳✳✳✳	✳✳✳✳✳
Esophageal injury (needing esophageal surgery)	Would Not Report	✳✳✳✳✳	✳✳✳✳✳	✳✳✳✳✳

The measures are specific to the type of surgery undergoing review. In cornea transplant surgery, for example, the success measures might include visual acuity better than 20/40 at ninety days postoperatively, and the complication measures might include cornea graft failure rate. After these rates are converted to a star grading system, patients will be able to compare surgeons based on these measures. Some surgeons will refuse to report, and patients will be left to wonder why. The following is an example of SurgiQuality's grading system for corneal transplant surgery:

	Surgeon A	Surgeon B	Surgeon C	Surgeon D
Procedure	Corneal Transplant	Corneal Transplant	Corneal Transplant	Corneal Transplant
Necessity?	Indicated	Indicated	Indicated	Indicated
# of Cases 2019	✱✱✱✱✱	✱✱✱✱	✱	Would Not Report
Visual Acuity 20/40 at 90 days Rate	✱	✱✱✱✱✱	✱✱✱	Would Not Report
Graft Failure Rate	✱	✱✱✱✱✱	✱✱✱	Would Not Report

As another example, for laparoscopic cholecystectomy (surgical removal of the gallbladder through scopes inserted into the abdomen), the measures might include bile duct injury rate (bile ducts allow bile to enter the intestine), conversion rate (how many times a surgeon was forced, because of bleeding or other circumstances, to convert from gallbladder removal through scopes to gallbladder removal through an abdominal incision), and mortality rate. The following is an example of SurgiQuality's grading system for laparoscopic cholecystectomy:

	Surgeon A	Surgeon B	Surgeon C	Surgeon D
Procedure	Lap Chole	Lap Chole	Lap Chole	Lap Chole
Necessity?	Indicated	Indicated	Indicated	Indicated
# of Cases 2019	✱✱✱✱	✱✱✱✱	✱✱✱✱✱	Would Not Report
Bile Duct Injury Rate	✱✱	✱✱✱✱	✱	Would Not Report
Conversion Rate	✱	✱✱✱	✱✱✱✱✱	Would Not Report
Mortality Rate	✱✱✱✱✱	✱✱✱	✱✱✱✱✱	Would Not Report

These measures will also change as the complexity of the procedure increases. The difficult gallbladder is a scenario in which cholecystectomy has an increased surgical risk, compared with standard cholecystectomy. Cholecystectomy can be made difficult by processes that either obscure bile duct anatomy (inflammation) or have difficult operative exposure (due to obesity or scarring from prior upper abdominal surgery).

In situations like these, the measures would be limited to a subset of the total cases. As an example, instead of the number of all cholecystectomy cases the previous year, the measure would ask for only the number of cases in obese patients the previous year. The measures may also change over time due to emerging technologies, such as robotic surgery and the use of navigation systems.

In order to clear any confusion patients have about their condition and possible surgical complications, SurgiQuality's concierge educates them on the measures used for their case. Empowered with smart information, consumers will make well-informed decisions.

SurgiQuality Patient Dashboard

Surgeon options are ready for presentation once surgeon responses are transformed to star grades and out-of-pocket costs are determined from surgeon/facility pricing. The concierge presents these options, acting as an advocate and careful not to steer patients to one surgeon or the other. The ultimate decision on which surgeon to use is left to the patient, who is free to contact those who have rendered opinions on his or her case.

Coronavirus has pushed telemedicine from the shadows and under the spotlight. SurgiQuality is ready to meet the needs of patients who are embracing online platforms as a means to meet their medical needs. But rather than merely a temporary stand-in until the coronavirus coast is clear and patients can return to their appointments, SurgiQuality offers a permanent and powerful cutting-edge tool that gives patients unprecedented power over some of the most important decisions they'll ever have to make. Armed with outcomes data, patients can start to ask intelligent questions like never before.

The SurgiQuality Patient Dashboard is a tool for patients to make the most essential decisions about their procedures. Customized according to the objectives of the health plan, the dashboard lists surgeons that have rendered opinions on the case, site of service, and the total *patient* cost for each surgeon option. The cost presented is not the total cost of the procedure; instead, it is only the all-inclusive, out-of-pocket cost the patient will be responsible for. Patients are able to compare surgeons and prioritize what is important to them.

They can filter for surgeon, cost, star grade, or location.

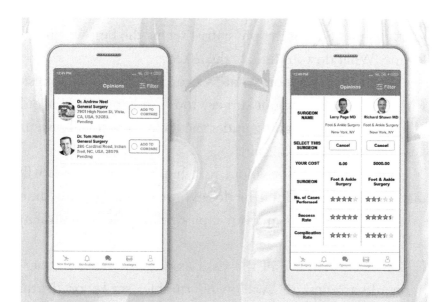

SurgiQuality patient dashboard for the patient, displaying different opinions from surgeons, the out-of-pocket cost, and outcome measures.

Patients are encouraged to contact surgeons and ask questions related to the surgical approach and the surgeon's experience. Once patients choose their surgeon, the concierge helps coordinate surgical scheduling and postoperative rehabilitation if necessary. Postoperatively, patient questionnaires are used to provide feedback to the surgeon and facility rendering care.

In Sara's case, she talked about her options with Brian over dinner.

"So what have you decided?" he asked.

"First off, I just want to thank you. You really helped me

get through this! I'm loving the SurgiQuality service. Based on everything I've researched, I'm going to avoid surgery, at least for now. Seeing the physiatrist seems the best way to go for me. What do you think?" she asked.

"You know I support whatever you decide. To be honest, I had my concerns about surgery too. I'm happy we'll avoid all the unknowns of going under the knife. Plus, it will save us a ton of money," Brian said.

"I'm being realistic about it. I hope the physiatrist will take care of things. But if he doesn't, we now have some time to save for surgery; I can even explore chiropractic treatment too," she said.

Sara reflected on all the risks associated with her operation—hoarseness or swallowing trouble, stroke or death, needing high-risk esophageal surgery, and spinal fluid leakage. Right now, she just didn't think surgery was necessary—especially considering what could happen. At the same, time she was glad the haze of uncertainty only made worse by the late-night, do-it-yourself internet research she performed prior to SurgiQuality had now lifted. She knew exactly the risks associated if she decided to undergo an operation.

From sleepless nights that were a result of both physical pain and anxiety to the peace of mind knowing she had her condition under control, Sara moved ahead with confidence. She knew she had made her decision based on objective, evidence-based information with surgical outcome measures tailored to her specific procedure. She had a Plan A, which was care under a physiatrist. And if that didn't work, she knew she had the resources to create a Plan B by continuing to make decisions based on her particular needs. With Surgi-Quality, her fear of the unknown was replaced with certainty and calm that she had a patient advocate literally in the palm of her hand.

Integration with Health Plans

The SurgiQuality solution integrates into existing solutions that public and private insurance carriers currently use.

Employer-Sponsored Health Plans

Most Americans today derive their health insurance coverage from employer-sponsored health plans. As previously mentioned, these can be either fully insured or self-insured. The self-insured health plans can be broken down into those managed by the insurance carrier (administrative services only, or ASO) and those managed by the employer through a third party (third-party administrator, or TPA). The annual premiums for these services are increasing with no end in sight. The rate at which costs are going up and their amount are simply not sustainable for employers and their employees. Something must be done.

SurgiQuality can help fully insured health plans ensure that members connect with best-in-class surgeons who operate in a cost-efficient environment. Similarly, self-insured health plans gain similar benefits, along with decreased costs from price competition.

Conclusion

The SurgiQuality solution is beneficial to patients, primary care physicians, surgeons, surgery centers, hospitals, employers, and health plans. The platform satisfies the quadruple aim:

- Enhancing patient experience
- Improving population health
- Reducing costs
- Improving the work life of healthcare providers, including clinicians and staff

In summary, SurgiQuality provides many advantages for the following groups:

Patients

- Personalized concierge
- Peer review to validate medical necessity
- Consumerism tools to comparison shop for price and quality
- Potential zero-deductible options

Primary Care Physicians

- Tool to refer patients to best-in-class surgeons

Employers

- Value-based healthcare
- Lower costs

CHAPTER 6

MEASUREMENTS OF SURGEON'S PROCEDURE-SPECIFIC OUTCOMES

Carl H. Snyderman, MD, MBA, & Erin McKean, MD, MBA

Introduction

A commitment to quality is a primary driver for healthcare and is a shared responsibility of all healthcare providers. Although there is recognition of the importance of measuring quality, there is lack of consensus on what to measure and how it relates to outcomes. When addressing surgical outcomes, the lens of quality can be applied at multiple levels of a healthcare system from the entire enterprise to the individual. From the perspective of the patient, the overriding question is: "What outcomes can I expect for this operation with this surgeon at this hospital?" This chapter will explore different aspects of surgical quality with an emphasis on the individual surgeon and specific procedure.

What Is Quality?

Although quality can be difficult to define, it is obvious when it is not present. Multiple definitions have been proposed. The

Institute of Medicine/National Academy of Medicine defines quality as "the degree to which health services for individuals and populations increase the likelihood of desired health outcomes and are consistent with professional knowledge." The Agency for Healthcare Research and Quality (AHRQ) defines quality as "doing the right thing (getting the medicines, tests, and counseling you need), doing it at the right time (when you need them), and doing it in the right way with your healthcare providers using the appropriate test or procedure)." It further explains that using the appropriate test or procedure to achieve the best possible results means avoiding their underuse, avoiding their overuse, and eliminating their misuse. In his article, "The Strategy That Will Fix Healthcare," Michael Porter and Thomas Lee state that "the only true measures of quality are the outcomes that matter to patients."

Why Should We Care?

There are a multitude of reasons to care about quality and its measurement. The primary driver is the desire to improve the outcomes of surgical care. Proper counseling of patients regarding the risks and benefits of a treatment is an essential part of informed consent. This means providing data that is interpretable and relevant to the point of care. What are the outcomes in your hands? Transparency allows patients to compare institutions and make a more informed choice. In a rapidly evolving and competitive market, the ability to provide surgeon or hospital-specific quality data may provide a marketing advantage and raises the bar for the community.

Increasingly, quality outcomes are being linked to payment through "pay for performance" programs derived from value-based purchasing. Examples include denial of payment for a "never event" or early readmission following surgery. These programs often tie reimbursements to quality metrics, as well as reductions in total cost of care.

Finally, the measurement of quality is important because patients and other advocacy groups care. Increasingly, the government, non-governmental healthcare organizations, consumer advocacy groups, and websites rate hospitals and physicians based on their outcomes. In the absence of data, evaluations are subjective and prone to bias.

Quality Is a Keystone Habit

Some important habits, called *keystone habits* by Charles Duhigg in his *The Power of Habit: Why We Do What We Do in Life and Business*, cause other habits to flourish, resulting in a change in culture.

For healthcare, quality provides the foundation, and attention to quality is a keystone habit that influences every other aspect of healthcare. It provides a "true north" compass that keeps the focus on the patient and is a tiebreaker when considering the repercussions of change. A hospital that has built a culture of sustained quality improvement can be expected to have processes in place that promote superior outcomes.

Keystone habits may also be relevant for the individual surgeon. There is conflicting evidence, however, whether superior outcomes are generalizable. For example, a highly ranked surgeon may demonstrate superior outcomes across a wide range of procedures. On the other hand, proficiency in a specific procedure does not necessarily confirm proficiency in other procedures. It may depend on how closely the procedures are related.

The Value Equation

Quality cannot be considered in isolation; it is part of the value equation:

$$Value = (Quality + Service)/Cost$$

Value is defined by Porter and Lee as "health outcomes [that matter to patients] achieved per dollar spent." This includes all the providers for an entire patient event. It is obvious from the equation that value can be maximized by increasing quality or service or both while controlling costs.

Patients must consider multiple factors when choosing a surgeon for their operation. These factors will vary depending on the values of the patients and can only be discovered through an open dialogue with the surgeon that explores their preferences. Although objective data are valuable in making a decision, they do not provide a complete picture, and other less tangible factors may be considered.

How Is Quality Assessed?

It is difficult for patients to assess the quality of surgery since it is a service that can't be experienced prior to use. Value is dominated by intangible elements, and the outcome may not be readily apparent. Additionally, patients are part of the experience, and people other than the surgeon affect the surgical experience.

The collection of data allows us to provide a more objective assessment of surgical outcomes. Surgical data can be categorized as qualitative or quantitative. Qualitative data consists of continuous variables such as quality of life, patient satisfaction, or relief of symptoms. In contrast, quantitative data consists of discrete variables such as survival, tumor recurrence, or complication. Surgical outcomes are often reported as single events, such as a mortality or complication. Near misses are an important type of outcome that are frequently ignored but extremely valuable. They are indicators of near failures and not lucky misses. A famous example is the Space Shuttle *Columbia*. It burned up from foam insulation that separated from the fuel tank, although that had been a regular occurrence in previous shuttle launches before disaster struck.[7]

Assessment of quality data is easier for common, high-volume procedures that are standardized. For rare, complex procedures, these data are often lacking, or there is heterogeneity in the surgical procedure.

Selection of Quality Metrics

Measures of quality can be categorized into clinical pathway measures (structure of care, process of care, outcome of care, and economic measures of care) and patient-reported measures (patient-reported treatment outcomes, health-related quality of life measures, and patient satisfaction).

Examples of possible quality metrics are listed in table 6.1. Metrics may be selected at different levels of care, ranging from the institution to the individual surgeon. AHRQ provides helpful resources for community collaboratives by highlighting national initiatives, defining roles and responsibilities for organizations developing metrics, and suggesting reporting criteria. Surgeons do not work in isolation. Increasingly, healthcare (including surgery) is a team activity, requiring the collective expertise of multiple individuals. A single metric may not capture this dynamic, and it may be necessary to consider a family of metrics at different levels.

Table 6.1. Possible quality metrics at all levels of a healthcare system.

Hospital	Length of stay Mortality Readmission Comparative costs
Surgery (all specialties)	Return to operating room SCIP (Surgical Care Improvement Project) compliance Operating room dictations Operating room delays Standardization of materials, devices Standardization of processes
Surgical Sub-Specialty/ Division	Survival rate Diagnostic error Delayed treatment Appropriate treatment Postoperative infection Postoperative hemorrhage Clinical care pathway utilization Documentation
Surgeon	Time to appointment Patient satisfaction Duration of operation Specific complication rate Blood loss and use of transfusions Pain medication usage Antibiotic usage

Procedure-Specific Metrics

Each surgical specialty struggles with finding the appropriate metrics for specific procedures or diagnoses. Reviews of the literature reveal a wide variety of metrics for different procedures, primarily consisting of clinical outcomes and process measures (Table 6.2). Capturing these metrics is often not practical, however, and data is frequently not available for comparison of individual surgeons and institutions. Although it is tempting to select simple metrics that are easy to measure, they may not reflect the entirety of the factors of the patient experience that are responsible for a good outcome. Risk stratification of patients based on the severity of illness, complexity of surgery, and co-morbidities may be necessary to allow a valid comparison of outcomes.

Among clinical pathway measures, surgical volume is used frequently. Generally, there is a positive relationship between surgical volume and outcomes for multiple surgical procedures, most notably colorectal cancer, bariatric surgery, and breast cancer. Despite concentration of surgical volume in Centers of Excellence, however, there exists considerable variation in surgical outcomes across geographic locations and operative volume. Prior literature has suggested that the volume-outcome relationship is specific to a particular procedure. For rare complex procedures where there is insufficient data, there may also be value in assessing surgeon volume for related procedures (halo effect).

Table 6.2. Quality measures for ventral hernia repair

(adapted from Sun BJ, Kamal RN, Lee GK, Nazerali RS. Quality measures in ventral hernia repair: a systematic review. Hernia. 2018;22(6):1023-1032).

Source	Category	Measure
AHS quality collaborative	Outcome	Revision surgery (30d)
AHS quality collaborative	Outcome	Hospital readmission within (30d)
AHS quality collaborative	Outcome	Emergency room visit (30d)
AHS quality collaborative	Outcome	Postoperative pain assessment
AHS quality collaborative	Outcome	Postoperative functional status assessment
AHRQ NQMC	Outcome	Accidental puncture or laceration
AHRQ NQMC	Process	On-time prophylactic antibiotics
NQF QPS	Outcome	Reclosure of postoperative disruption of wound
NQF QPS	Outcome	Surgical site infection
QPP/PQRS	Process	Appropriate antibiotic selection
QPP/PQRS	Process	Venous thromboembolism prophylaxis
QPP/PQRS	Process	Postoperative medication reconciliation
QPP/PQRS	Process	Follow-up plan for increased BMI
QPP/PQRS	Process	Tobacco use assessment and counseling
QPP/PQRS	Process	Preoperative risk assessment

AHS: American Hernia Society; AHRQ: Agency for Healthcare Research and Quality; NQMC: National Quality Measures Clearinghouse; NQF: National Quality Forum; QPS: Quality Positioning System; QPP: Quality Payment Program; PQRS: Physician Quality Reporting System; BMI: body mass index

Patient-reported outcomes may be the most relevant metrics but can be difficult to measure. Categories of patient-reported outcomes include health-related quality of life, functional status, symptoms, health behaviors, and patient experience. Due to the interaction of multiple factors and the contribution of many individuals to the surgical experience, it may be difficult to isolate key factors.

Each surgery has its own specific risks and expected outcomes, dependent on the underlying pathology. For common, high-volume procedures, these are simpler to define. For complex procedures with greater variation in technique, however, it can be difficult to define a common metric for comparison. In such situations, we can extrapolate from closely related procedures or use a less specific metric.

Surgical Competency

At the most basic level, surgeons are credentialed by individual hospitals as competent to perform specific procedures. Generally, surgeons are credentialed upon entry to surgical practice, undergo periodic re-credentialing, and are credentialed for new procedures and techniques as they are developed. This process varies tremendously across hospitals, and there is little uniformity. Specialty societies may provide guidelines for specific procedures or techniques such as robotic surgery, but these are not universally adopted. Due to rapid evolution of surgical techniques and introduction of new technologies, it is a daunting challenge for hospitals to monitor surgical performance. Further, smaller hospitals lack adequate mentors for surgeons learning new techniques.

There is great interest in developing objective methods that can measure surgical competency. Although there has been much discussion regarding declining function (cognitive and physical) with the aging surgeon, age alone is not a good discriminator, and longitudinal data linking cognitive function and performance are lacking.

Objective measures of cognitive and physical performance are generally not mandated unless there are concerns about performance, and such tests are otherwise considered investigational. Review of surgical videos using Objective Structured Assessment Tool Skills (OSATS) shows promise, with the ability to differentiate surgeons based on experience. Key operative indicators can be selected as general indicators of quality. For example, mobilizing the gallbladder neck from the gallbladder bed of the liver before clipping and transecting the cystic artery and duct during laparoscopic cholecystectomy is considered the critical view of safety in avoiding inadvertent bile duct injury and is not verifiable without video review.

CHAPTER 7

MALPRACTICE CLAIMS AND SURGEON RATINGS

Sapan Shah, MD, JD

When I was in medical school, I did my internal medicine and cardiology rotations at Cleveland Clinic. Some of my attendings (academic faculty ultimately responsible for the care of the patient) knew I went to law school before medical school and would discuss malpractice cases or liability issues when things were slow.

One attending told me a story:

A famous cardiologist had seen a longtime patient in the hospital whose ECG (electrocardiogram) showed a classic sign for pulmonary embolism—S1Q3T3. (Pulmonary embolism is a condition where a clot impedes blood flow to parts of the lung.)

The cardiologist knew the low specificity and sensitivity of this sign and decided not to start anticoagulation in the context of the patient's clinical picture. (Anticoagulation involves administering medications, either by mouth or intravenously, that help dissolve clots.)

A few hours later, the patient's condition deteriorated, and a CT scan showed a large pulmonary embolism (clot) requiring emergent embolectomy (procedure to remove the clot). The cardiologist called the patient's wife and told her about the ECG finding and that, at that time, he hadn't thought it was a PE (pulmonary embolus). He also told her that he was wrong and that now, her husband needed emergent surgery. He asked her to come to the hospital immediately and told her, "I will meet you at the front entrance." He sat with her throughout the surgery.

The patient unfortunately did not survive the procedure. The cardiologist gave his condolences to the wife. Even in that moment of great sadness, she told the cardiologist, "I am so grateful for all of the care you provided my husband. Thank you for everything over the years."

So many questions went through my mind when I heard this story as a medical student:

- Was this famous cardiologist actually not so good?

- What does "good" even mean … getting it right every time?

- What does the reputation of a particular institution mean for the outcomes or quality of care or both for what you can expect?

- Was low sensitivity and specificity of the ECG finding protective for the cardiologist?

- How much must it have mattered to the patient's wife that the cardiologist called her, met her at the front of the hospital, and sat with her through the surgery?

- What physicians did that then? Who does that even now?

I have thought about this story so many more times over the years because it highlights the many factors that go into medical malpractice liability, and I will come back to it throughout this chapter.

My career has been focused on representing the interests of physicians in risk issues and malpractice insurance placements. Through this work, I have seen thousands of curriculum vitae and histories of malpractice claim losses and malpractice claim payments. Physicians are always interested in how they stack up against their peers: "Is that a normal number of claims for my experience and specialty?"

Does analysis of malpractice claim information, both frequency (how many claims) and severity (how much was paid), relate to a physician's skill level, patient outcomes, and surgeon proficiency? In addition, can where physicians graduated from or trained indicate anything about their quality of care, outcomes, or malpractice risk? In my experience, analysis of malpractice claim information is only partially helpful and effective only in weeding out a small percentage of physicians who provide poor care. By itself, this analysis is ineffective in differentiating 80 percent of physicians in a particular specialty.

The lack of sensitivity of malpractice claim information starts with its own complexity. On the legal side, medical malpractice requires four components:

1. **Duty:** The physician must have a physician-patient relationship with the patient.

2. **Breach:** The physician must breach or deviate from the standard of care.

3. **Injury:** The patient must suffer an injury.

4. **Causation:** The patient's injury must be caused by the physician's breach.

In practice these legal requirements intersect with jurisdictional nuances and more subjective dynamics when you consider patient relationships with their physicians, physicians' own styles and demeanors (their bedside manner), as well as acuity and types of cases particular physicians deal with on a day-to-day basis.

Did the patient's wife not sue the cardiologist because of the low sensitivity and specificity of the ECG finding? Or did she refrain, rather, because of the longstanding relationship? Or was it the great care and compassion shown in the cardiologist's transparency and time spent at her side?

Since so much subjectivity can go into the filing of a claim, the utility of individual claims as prognostic of physician skill is also limited. I represented an OB/GYN who practiced thirty-seven years and had only one claim in his career. The claim alleged that he delayed delivery by cesarean section surgery for a mother whose fetus was experiencing distress, noted by fetal heart tracings.

The OB/GYN was covering for a colleague, and the patient was unknown to him. In fact, he counseled the patient several times that a C-section was needed and documented the patient's unwillingness to move forward. Ultimately the patient changed her mind and allowed a C-section.

Unfortunately, the baby was born with a neurological injury, directly a result of the delay. Because the case was being tried in an unfavorable jurisdiction and because of discovery issues, a settlement of $1.5 million was made to end litigation. Although the payment was very high, I do not think this case says anything about the skill level or proficiency of this OB/GYN. Further, it more aptly can be considered an outlier scenario in an otherwise wonderful career for him.

If one claim alone is not telling, what can we make of more frequent cases against a physician? Surgical specialties in particular have higher claim frequency due to their inherent invasive nature and potential for complications.

One review of a large national malpractice carrier's claim data found that roughly 55 percent of physicians in internal medicine and its subspecialties were projected to face a malpractice claim by the age of forty-five years, and 89 percent by the age of sixty-five years. In contrast, 80 percent of physicians in surgical specialties (including general surgery) and 74 percent of physicians in obstetrics and gynecology were projected to face a claim by the age of forty-five years.

Can the number of claims a surgeon has indicate anything about his or her skill level or likelihood of good outcomes?

A few years ago, I represented an orthopedic surgeon who also did spine surgeries. He was at the tail end of his career and had the worst loss history of any client we have ever had. He had been sued more than fifty times, or 1.5 claims per year, in his career, paying out millions in total damages, not including defense costs. His malpractice claims history was a true outlier in the market, and reasonable people would avoid getting a surgery done by him if they were aware of his history. I also represented many other spine surgeons, each of whom has been repeatedly sued. These other spine surgeons had claims rates less than 0.5 per year, or one claim for every two to three years of practice. Taken together, this malpractice claim information would tell us to confidently exclude the fifty-claim surgeon but perhaps not help with discerning amongst the others.

The Council for Affordable Quality Healthcare (CAQH) is a nonprofit organization that has developed a database for physicians to eliminate duplicative paperwork with organizations that require professional and practice information for claims administration, credentialing, directory services, and more. Malpractice claim information is also included in the database. Physicians provide access of their profile to insurance companies and hospitals for credentialing purposes.

The National Practitioner Data Bank (NPDB) is a repository of reports containing information on medical malpractice payments and certain adverse actions related to healthcare practitioners, providers, and suppliers. Established by Congress in 1986, it is a workforce tool that prevents practitioners from moving state to state without disclosure or discovery of previous damaging performance. Here excessive claims or patterns of claims may trigger follow-up questions from reviewers, but in practice, we have seen very few circumstances where physician credentialing has been declined singularly due to claims histories. This is especially the case in underserved or rural areas where physician presence is highly sought after.

Other proxy data for surgical skill and correlation with complication or malpractice risk are yet to be substantiated. Given the somewhat private nature of claims data, its low frequency, and the dispersion of physicians throughout fifty states, we have limited information about the skill level of graduates from a particular medical school or residency program versus another. One study in 2003 did find "consistent differences in malpractice experience among medical schools" but looked at data from only three states and had to exclude forty-seven medical schools because of insufficient data. Here, as well, a small number of schools showed the correlation of consistently higher claims frequency amongst their graduates. In this regard, can we really say anything about discerning malpractice risk in graduates from the vast majority of schools?

At first glance, one would expect the esteem and reputation of certain schools or training programs to connect to the quality of most of its graduates. Nevertheless, how useful is relative reputation or rankings between the top 60-70 percent of programs in discerning the quality of an individual surgeon or physician? Further, when a patient undergoes a procedure, it is a particular surgeon and not the medical school or residency program he or she graduated from that is performing that surgery.

Specific evaluation of your own surgeon—his or her experience, complication rates, and outcomes—is likely more predictive for a patient than which medical school he or she attended. I represent a vascular surgeon who has never had a claim for malpractice and graduated from an average medical school. Her colleagues in other surgical specialties have repeatedly recognized her for her work in correcting operative complications and artery damage in the context of knee surgeries and abdominal surgeries. Such emergent proficiency is a wonderful surgical quality, which is why her colleagues readily refer cases to her and are interested in her presence in the hospital when they are operating. This is perhaps much more important information in assessing her strength as a vascular surgeon.

For patients without such professional insight, applications such as the SurgiQuality solution can provide advocacy and information to guide patients in reviewing physicians and surgeons for quality. SurgiQuality queries the surgeon's electronic medical record to corroborate outcomes and complications data for participating surgeons, providing patients with relevant information to guide their decisions

Such outcome granularity specific for a procedure is simply uninterpretable from malpractice claim information.

While malpractice claim information cannot always say a great deal about physician quality, physicians can do many things to improve or mitigate their claims experience. Certainly documentation, sound record keeping, and clear communication are very protective for physicians. Documentation helps strengthen defense of claims when they arise, where communication can potentially diffuse difficult situations, so claims are not filed in the first place.

In the context of surgical specialties, recommendations and consultation with peers about surgical indications or difficult procedures can also be very helpful in mitigating complications and adverse outcomes. Pre-operative peer review in the SurgiQuality platform is an excellent example of this. We represent a large OB/GYN group that has physicians with a range of ages and experience. The lead physician consistently looks at surgical schedules for potentially difficult cases and offers senior physicians to scrub in with younger associate physicians. Such consultation, active assistance, or even a simple discussion can help surgeons mitigate the types of injuries or events that can be the heart of malpractice claims.

Ultimately, malpractice liability is only somewhat correlated with the quality or competency of an individual physician or surgeon. The qualities that make good physicians—deep knowledge of their specialty, experience, outcomes, focus, compassion, care, bedside manner, advocacy for the patient—are not easily objectively measured in our current healthcare system. Additionally, while we as physicians have an awareness to see and evaluate these characteristics within our peers, it is very difficult for patients to evaluate these aspects in us generally. Patients can better understand and do appreciate long-term relationships, respect, diligent care, and true compassion. When I think over the cardiologist story again, I think the wife was so appreciative of these elements of the cardiologist's care she never even considered looking into the ECG finding.

CHAPTER 8

SURGIQUALITY CASE STUDIES

Sanjay Prasad, MD, FACS and Lauren Pritchard

The following are examples of how SurgiQuality has empowered patients with smart information to make well-informed choices.

If the condition warrants, patients may be referred to a surgeon, whom we will refer to as the "index surgeon." He or she may order blood tests, X-rays, and specialized diagnostic tests. Imaging studies like a CT or MRI scan may also be recommended. After reviewing these tests, the index surgeon makes a diagnosis and typically recommends treatment options.

Steve

Chief Complaint: Steve was forty-one years old and had lately suffered from intermittent episodes of disorientation, hallucinations, and fainting spells.

Recent History: Steve went to see his doctor, who ordered an MRI. It revealed an abnormality in the temporal lobe of his brain.

Index Surgeon: Thinking Steve's condition was from a viral infection, his index surgeon, a local neurologist and neurosurgeon, treated him with intravenous anti-viral medications.

Steve then obtained another opinion from a local neurosurgeon. Because of his persistent symptoms, the physician determined that it was a tumor and not a viral infection. He referred him to an academic center, quite a distance away for the surgery the following week.

SurgiQuality Process: Over a holiday weekend, a concierge helped gather medical records and imaging, upload the records to the HIPAA-compliant cloud, and send the records to multiple board-certified neurosurgeons.

SurgiQuality Results: Four board-certified academic and non-academic neurosurgeons reviewed the case and rendered opinions.

1. All four neurosurgeons highly recommended against major surgery.

2. One neurosurgeon stated that further testing, such as a needle biopsy, was needed.

3. Two others recommended, rather than surgery, a repeat MRI scan sometime later to monitor progress.

4. The fourth neurosurgeon opined that the patient definitely had a viral infection and recommended no surgery.

Outcome: Despite the opinions, Steve traveled to the academic center. That morning, he had a repeat MRI scan, and then was put in the operating room. Luckily, the MRI showed the lesion had disappeared, and the procedure was aborted.

The patient was so close to having a procedure that was not necessary. Just think of all the risks of brain surgery, the possible complications, and the potential mortality, not to mention the exorbitant costs including for the operating room, postoperative recovery, and time lost from work.

Natasha

Chief Complaint: Natasha, eighty-six years old, was living alone and fell in her home.

History: Natasha had a history of heart failure and atrial fibrillation. She was living independently and fell in her home. Emergency medical services was called, and she was transported to the nearest hospital. An X-ray revealed a hip fracture involving the femoral neck.

Index Surgeon: The hospital orthopedic surgeon recommended palliative care and opioids for pain control. He did not recommend surgery because of Natasha's advanced age and risk of general anesthesia, especially considering her history of heart failure and atrial fibrillation. She would have to live her remaining years immobile in a nursing home and addicted to opioids.

SurgiQuality Process: The concierge helped gather records, upload them to the HIPAA-compliant cloud, and send them to multiple orthopedic surgeons.

SurgiQuality Results: An anesthesiologist in Natasha's family suggested an alternative to general anesthesia, called regional anesthesia, where only a portion of her body would be anesthetized. He believed this would be safer for her. Natasha contacted SurgiQuality to find a nearby surgeon. In particular, she was in search of a surgeon that would offer regional rather than general anesthesia, which would align with her family member's recommendation.

Six orthopedic surgeons were contacted.

1. A board-certified orthopedic surgeon who had twenty years of experience with hip surgery, was in Natasha's area and stated that regional anesthesia, as suggested by the family member, was his preferred approach.

2. Five other board-certified orthopedic surgeons who had a special interest in hip surgery recommended proceeding with general anesthesia and take the inherent risks.

Outcome: Rather than be confined to bed the rest of her life and addicted to opioids, Natasha decided to have the procedure under regional anesthesia. The procedure lasted forty-five minutes, and she was able to walk that day after surgery! She is now fully mobile without assistive devices and can climb stairs without assistance. The patient continues to have a productive and active life.

Without SurgiQuality, Natasha's ability to find a specialized surgeon with experience operating under regional anesthesia would have been impossible, and she would have had to spend the rest of her days in a nursing home, immobile, and addicted to opioids.

Pablo

Chief Complaint: Pablo, sixty-two years old, suffered a right ankle fracture.

History: Pablo has diabetes and had a heart attack. At the age of nineteen, he had a right ankle fracture.

Pablo's recent injury occurred when he slipped on ice. Swelling and pain persisted, despite use of a compression bandage. Four months later, increasing pain while playing golf led to an X-ray that revealed a right ankle fracture involving the fibula.

Index Surgeon: Pablo was seen multiple times by an orthopedic surgeon who recommended surgery with insertion of a plate to repair the non-healing fracture.

SurgiQuality Process: A concierge helped gather records, upload them to the HIPAA-compliant cloud, and send them to multiple orthopedic surgeons.

SurgiQuality Results: Eight board-certified orthopedic surgeons reviewed Pablo's records and rendered opinions on SurgiConnect.

1. Three surgeons reported that surgery was not necessary and would be dangerous from the increased risk of infection given Pablo's history of diabetes, risk of delayed healing, and risk of developing a diabetic foot. They recommended a magnetic bone stimulator instead.

2. Five surgeons recommended surgery

Outcome: Pablo decided to have surgery.

Because of the SurgiQuality service, he was able to benefit from multiple opinions without traveling. Also, Pablo was better able to understand how his diabetes increased surgical risks.

Cristina

Chief Complaint: Cristina was fifty-two years old with increasingly painful and uncomfortable bowel movements.

Index Surgeon: Her local GYN diagnosed a vaginal hernia, where the rectum herniates into the vagina, related to her history of multiple vaginal births. Surgery was recommended at the local hospital. Cristina was part of a medical cost-sharing program, and the total price quoted was $35,000, which included the surgeon, anesthesia, and facility fees. Because of the high price for the surgery, Cristina wished to explore other surgeons to see if she could have the procedure for a lower price.

SurgiQuality Process: A concierge helped gather records, upload them to the HIPAA-compliant cloud, and send them to multiple board-certified GYN surgeons.

SurgiQuality Results: Seven board-certified GYN surgeons rendered opinions and reported pricing.

1. All seven recommended surgery,
2. The least expensive with high quality measures reported an all-inclusive price of $7,200.

Outcome: Armed with pricing information, Cristina was able to negotiate pricing with her local doctor and her hospital to $12,500. Because of SurgiQuality, she was able to stay with the doctor of her choice and gain competitive pricing. The savings for the medical cost sharing plan was $22,500.

Veronica

Chief Complaint: Fifty-year-old Veronica suffered sudden loss of hearing on her left side.

Recent History: Veronica was treated with two steroid injections in the ear for presumed viral inflammation of the inner ear, with no improvement. An MRI revealed a small tumor on the nerves between the inner ear and the brain, consistent with a benign acoustic neuroma. The patient did not have dizziness or vertigo.

Index Surgeon: Because of the small size of the tumor, observation, rather than radiation or surgery, was recommended. A repeat MRI scan was also suggested in six months to establish the growth rate. (These tumors usually have an exceedingly slow rate of growth.)

SurgiQuality Process: A concierge helped gather records, upload them to the HIPAA-compliant cloud, and send them to multiple neurosurgeons and neuro-otologists (specialized ENT) surgeons.

SurgiQuality Results: Three surgeons reviewed her case:

1. Two agreed with the index surgeon that no surgery was indicated.

2. One recommended surgery to remove the tumor because of its small size.

Outcome: The patient decided observation would be her best choice with a repeat MRI scan, confirming the index surgeon's opinion.

Conclusion

These patients' success stories show how important Surgi-Quality is throughout the surgical process. Patients now have access to multiple opinions based on outcomes and price that help ensure they receive high quality and appropriate care and treatment.

The global coronavirus pandemic has hit the reset button on US healthcare. But beyond medicine, people are modifying their behavior in reaction to the coronavirus that aligns with their beliefs and needs. On one end of the extreme are those who take drastic precautions. And on the other end are those that do not take any at all. The ways patients are adjusting to healthcare's new normal reflect their general approach to coronavirus.

Regardless of your response to the pandemic, all patients have been affected by it in one or more of the following ways:

First, some have been directly struck down by COVID-19 and will require treatment for the long-term physical and psychological consequences of the virus.

Second, many had loved ones who succumbed to COVID-19.

Third, some postponed their non-urgent surgeries because of widespread lockdowns and perhaps now have conditions that have worsened as a result.

Fourth, patients avoided receiving medical care because of mandatory lockdowns or concerns of personal safety or both.

Last, all of us are navigating a healthcare system with new protocols that quickly change based on COVID-19 infection and hospitalization rates, the widespread economic fallout from the pandemic on the healthcare system, and the ever-changing decisions of public healthcare officials and politicians. On the bright side, mass vaccination and herd immunity will have a major positive impact.

Next, add to the preceding the pre-pandemic marketing landscape that continues today where hospitals, academic institutions, and healthcare facilities spend billions selling the public on what they have to offer. Clearly, these organizations are on an unending mission of reminding you they exist. This expresses itself in diverse forms such as hospital e-newsletters, glossy print magazines, and the CD you receive that contains your CT and MRI results ... as well as hospital contact information.

You'll see commercials on YouTube where sick boys and girls are receiving breakthrough treatments at a self-identified "world-renowned" children's hospital. You'll spot hospital logos in sports arenas. You'll drive by massive construction projects resulting in magnificent facility facelifts and new wings declaring to a community that the hospital is the epicenter of cutting-edge and successful healing. Next are local, state, and national rankings from various publications boldly announcing that a medical facility is "The Best!" to varying degrees of superiority: best in its city, state, the country, and even the whole world; best in a specialty; or best at practically everything.

The expensive and big marketing campaigns work. Hospital branding efforts embedding themselves in our subconscious play a role in the surgical decisions we make. They speak to our tendency to rely on snap decisions when presented with too much information. And even patients that make an explicit attempt to research their hospitals and doctors often find themselves drowning under a sea of information overload.

In the end, it's no wonder why patients often defer their final decision to others, whether it be their primary care doctor or practice or their friends and family. Without a clear path to evaluate surgeon quality, leaving it to the experts or trusted family and friends seems the most reliable route. But when it comes to friends and family, following their recommendations, while comforting, is a far cry from relying on broad and prudent empirical evidence. And when it comes to expert referrals, as you've read throughout these pages, forces are at play that have nothing to do with what's most important: surgical outcomes.

Added to all this is the greater financial burden patients are bearing by way of the cost of higher deductibles and co-pays and out-of-network specialists. Pre-pandemic, patient healthcare costs increased year over year. The coronavirus will no doubt result in more expensive healthcare for everyone. Today, with shrinking personal and household incomes and swelling healthcare costs, many patients simply cannot afford to blindly follow the recommendations of others, particularly if there are less expensive and more effective options. But up to this point, patients have had no means to skillfully and efficiently determine the full range of choices they have, let alone their quality.

SurgiQuality gives patients unprecedented resources to make what are often the most important decisions in their lives. Our platform is designed to provide patients outcome-driven information that emphasizes transparency of both quality and cost. With evidence-based information specific to your procedure, SurgiQuality puts you in the driver's seat of your healthcare decisions and at the same time makes your evaluation process more effective. Rather than experiencing information overload that results in you deferring your decisions to others, you have an expert advocate—someone that will clear away the clutter and highlight the information most relevant to you.

The promise of the Information Age is more transparency and resources for all those connected to their devices. But with so much data zooming through cyberspace and appearing on our smartphones and computer screens, the downside is what we scroll through is equal parts truth and misinformation. And we're often left with no way to discern which one is which.

When it comes to our healthcare, most Americans are not doctors or medical experts. So when we're confronted with a major medical need, how do we even begin to make well-informed decisions? The harsh reality is most of us have been in the dark. And the financial and physical toll the pandemic has placed on patients has further pushed us into the shadows. But just as video conferencing, cloud computing, and fast internet have allowed employees to work remotely unlike never before, today's technology offers breakthrough solutions so that we can thrive under healthcare's new normal. SurgiQuality casts a bright light of positive disruption that illuminates a path for patients to wisely navigate the pandemic age on our terms. Through the customized service SurgiQuality provides, patients will reach a destination that best aligns with their preferences, needs, and values.

NOTES

Introduction

2   **according to the World Health Organization**
Alexa Lardieri, "WHO: Nearly All Coronavirus Deaths
in Europe Are People Aged 60 and Older," U.S. News &
World Report online, April 2, 2020, https://www.usnews.
com/news/world-report/articles/2020-04-02/who-
nearly-all-coronavirus-deaths-in-europe-are-people-aged-
60-and-older.

3   **the exchange of respiratory droplets**   CDC
website, "Ways COVID-19 Spreads," updated October
28, 2020, https://www.cdc.gov/coronavirus/2019-ncov/
prevent-getting-sick/how-covid-spreads.html.

3   **pediatric multi-organ inflammatory syndrome**
Jorge L. Ortiz, "Almost All Kids Are Treatable:
What Parents Should Know: New COVID-Related
Inflammatory Disease," USA Today online, May
13, 2020, https://www.usatoday.com/story/news/
nation/2020/05/13/coronavirus-what-parents-should-
know-new-covid-related-disease/3121271001/.

4	**Several vaccines were developed**	Food and Drug Administration, "FDA Takes Key Action in Fight against COVID-19 by Issuing Emergency Use Authorization for First COVID-19 Vaccine," news release, December 11, 2020, https://www.fda.gov/news-events/press-announcements/fda-takes-key-action-fight-against-covid-19-issuing-emergency-use-authorization-first-covid-19; Food and Drug Administration, "FDA Takes Additional Action in Fight against COVID-19 by Issuing Emergency Use Authorization for Second COVID-19 Vaccine," news release, December 18, 2020, https://www.fda.gov/news-events/press-announcements/fda-takes-additional-action-fight-against-covid-19-issuing-emergency-use-authorization-second-covid; Food and Drug Administration, "FDA Issues Emergency Use Authorization for Third COVID-19 Vaccine," news release, February 27, 2021, https://www.fda.gov/news-events/press-announcements/fda-issues-emergency-use-authorization-third-covid-19-vaccine.

4	**Operation Warp Speed**	US Department of Defense website, "Coronavirus: Operation Warp Speed," accessed April 14, 2021, https://www.defense.gov/Explore/Spotlight/Coronavirus/Operation-Warp-Speed/.

4	**The virus affects patients directly and indirectly**	Angela Cabotaje, "Why Does the Coronavirus Affect People So Differently?" US Medicine, May 6, 2020, https://rightasrain.uwmedicine.org/well/health/coronavirus-affects-people-differently.

4   **people who have survived severe COVID-19**
Jennifer Couzin-Frankel, "From 'Brain Fog' to Heart
Damage, COVID-19's Lingering Problems Alarm
Scientists," Science, July 31, 2021, https://www.
sciencemag.org/news/2020/07/brain-fog-heart-damage-
covid-19-s-lingering-problems-alarm-scientists.

Chapter 1

5   **urgent and emergency surgeries**   "Types of
Surgery," Johns Hopkins Medicine website, accessed May
17, 2021, https://www.hopkinsmedicine.org/health/
treatment-tests-and-therapies/types-of-surgery.

6   ***91.4 percent of all surgeries were non-urgent***
Meghan Prin, Jean Guglielminotti, Onias Mtalimanja,
et al., "Emergency-to-Elective Surgery Ratio: A Global
Indicator of Access to Surgical Care," World Journal of
Surgery, July 2018, 42(7):1971-1980, https://pubmed.
ncbi.nlm.nih.gov/29270649/.

7   **seven hundred billion dollars**   Eric Munoz,
William Munoz 3rd, and Leslie Wise, "National and
Surgical Health Care Expenditures, 2005-2025," Annals
of Surgery, February 2010, 251(2): 195-200, https://
pubmed.ncbi.nlm.nih.gov/20054269/.

7   **main motives for the mortarium**   Centers
for Medicare & Medicaid Services, "CMS Releases
Recommendations on Adult Elective Surgeries, Non-
Essential Medical, Surgical, and Dental Procedures
during COVID-19 Response," news release, March 18,
2020, https://www.cms.gov/newsroom/press-releases/
cms-releases-recommendations-adult-elective-surgeries-
non-essential-medical-surgical-and-dental.

7   **"Our ability to respond to patients**   Letter
to Jerome M. Adams from AHA, AAMC, CH, and
Federation of American Hospitals, US Surgeon General,
March 15, 2020, https://www.aha.org/system/files/
media/file/2020/03/aha-to-surgeon-general-elective-
surgeries-and-covid-19-3-15-2020.pdf.

9   **about a 50 percent reduction of patients**
Mario Gaudino, Joanna Chikwe, Irbaz Hameed,
et al., "Response of Cardiac Surgery Units to
COVID-19," Circulation, July 21, 2020, 142(3),
https://www.ahajournals.org/doi/10.1161/
CIRCULATIONAHA.120.047865.

9   **67 percent drop in gastric procedures**   Praveen
Kumar R. Bhat, Santosh Kumar K. Y., Chandrashekar
Sorake, and Ganaraj Kulamarva, "Gastrointestinal
Malignancies and the COVID 19 Pandemic: Evidence-
Based Triage to Surgery," *Journal of Gastrointestinal Surgery*,
September 15, 2020, 24(11), 2698-2699, https://www.
ncbi.nlm.nih.gov/pmc/articles/PMC7491593/.

10   **seasonal spikes of coronavirus**   "Frequent
Seasonal Coronavirus Reinfections Hint a Possibility
of Endemic COVID-19," Michigan News, University
of Michigan, March 25, 2021, https://news.umich.
edu/frequent-seasonal-coronavirus-reinfections-hint-at-
possibility-of-endemic-covid-19/.

12   **64.7 percent of the physicians surveyed**   Debra
Shute, "Physicians Say Up to 30% of Treatment
Unnecessary," HealthLeaders, September 7, 2017,
https://www.healthleadersmedia.com/strategy/
physicians-say-30-treatment-unnecessary.

12   ***Health in the 21st Century***   Francisco Contreras, MD, *Health in the 21st Century: Will Doctors Survive?*, Denver, CO: Nutri Books, 1997.

12   **17.7 percent on healthcare**   "National Health Expenditure Data," CMS, updated December 16, 2020, https://www.cms.gov/Research-Statistics-Data-and-Systems/Statistics-Trends-and-Reports/NationalHealthExpendData/NationalHealthAccountsHistorical.

12   **highest percent in the world**   "How Does the U.S. Healthcare System Compare to Other Countries?" Peter G. Peterson Foundation, July 14, 2020, https://www.pgpf.org/blog/2020/07/how-does-the-us-healthcare-system-compare-to-other-countries.

Chapter 2

24   **In 2020, the estimated median household income**   "Estimated Median Family Incomes for Fiscal Year (FY) 2020," US Department of Housing and Urban Development, April 1, 2020, https://www.huduser.gov/portal/datasets/il/il20/Medians2020r.pdf.

24   **average family health insurance deductible**   "How Much Does Individual Health Insurance Cost?" eHealth, updated November 24, 2020, https://www.ehealthinsurance.com/resources/individual-and-family/how-much-does-individual-health-insurance-cost.

24   **individual insurance deductible**   Ibid.

24   **78 percent of Americans live paycheck to paycheck**   Zack Friedman, "78% of Workers Live Paycheck to Paycheck," Forbes, January 11, 2019, https://www.forbes.com/sites/zackfriedman/2019/01/11/live-paycheck-to-paycheck-government-shutdown/?sh=5dc160744f10.

24   **66.5 percent of all US bankruptcies**   Josh Owens for Safehaven.com, "Medical Bankruptcy Is Killing the American Middle Class," Nasdaq, February 14, 2019, https://www.nasdaq.com/articles/medical-bankruptcy-is-killing-the-american-middle-class-2019-02-14.

25   **to qualify for an HSA**   "Health Savings Account (HSA)," HealthCare.gov, accessed April 13, 2021, https://www.healthcare.gov/glossary/health-savings-account-hsa/.

26   **possibility of economic hardship**   Carlos Dobkin, Amy Finkelstein, Raymond Kluender, and Matthew J. Notowidigdo, "Myth and Measurement: The Case of Medical Bankruptcies," *New England Journal of Medicine*, March 22, 2018, 878(12), 1076-1078, https://www.ncbi.nlm.nih.gov/pmc/articles/PMC5865642/.

26   **30 percent of all surgical procedures**   L. L. Leaps, "Unnecessary Surgery," *Health Services Research*, August 1989, 24(3), 351-407, https://www.ncbi.nlm.nih.gov/pmc/articles/PMC1065571/.

Chapter 3

29 **"Newsweek World's Best Hospitals,"** "World's Best Hospitals 2021, Newsweek, accessed April 13, 2021, https://www.newsweek.com/best-hospitals-2021/united-states.

29 **"America's Top 100 Hospitals,"** "America's Best Hospitals 2021: America's 250 Best Hospitals," Healthgrades, accessed April 13, 2021, https://www.healthgrades.com/quality/americas-best-hospitals?redirected=true.

29 **"Quality Award,"** "HealthInsight Quality Award," Comagine Health website, accessed April 13, 2021, https://healthinsight.org/quality-awards.

31 **study of 638,973 US surgeries** Yusuke Tsugawa, Justin B. Dimick, Anupam B. Jena, et al., "Comparison of Patient Outcomes of Surgeons Who Are US versus International Medical Graduates," *Annals of Surgery*, December 10, 2019, https://journals.lww.com/annalsofsurgery/Abstract/9000/Comparison_of_Patient_Outcomes_of_Surgeons_Who_Are.94747.aspx.

31 **physicians were trained in less than three years** John R. Raymond Sr., Joseph E. Kerschner, William J. Hueston, and Cheryl A. Maurana, "The Merits and Challenges of Three-Year Medical School Curricula Time for an Evidence-Based Discussion," *Academic Medicine*, October 2015, 90(10), 1318-1323, https://journals.lww.com/academicmedicine/fulltext/2015/10000/The_Merits_and_Challenges_of_Three_Year_Medical.17.aspx.

32   **Students, however, were satisfied**   Ibid.

32   **no significant differences in the clinical
        performance**   J. A. Hallock, J. A. Christensen,
        M. W. Denker, et al., "A Comparison of the Clinical
        Performance of Students in Three- and Four-Year
        Curricula," *Journal of Medical Education*, August
        1977, 52(8), 658-63, https://journals.lww.com/
        academicmedicine/Abstract/1977/08000/A_
        comparison_of_the_clinical_performance_of.6.aspx.

32   **fellowship-trained surgeons limit**   "What Does It
        Mean for a Doctor to Be Fellowship Trained?" Peconic Bay
        Medical Center website, September 9, 2015, https://www.
        pbmchealth.org/news-events/blog/what-does-it-mean-
        doctor-be-fellowship-trained.

34   ***U.S. News & World Report*'s listing**   "U.S. News
        & World Report Hospital Rankings & Ratings," U.S.
        News & World Report website, accessed April 13, 2021,
        https://health.usnews.com/best-hospitals.

34   **popular report's rating methodology**   U.S.
        News Staff, "FAQ: How and Why We Rank and Rate
        Hospitals," U.S. News & World Report, July 28, 2020,
        https://health.usnews.com/health-care/best-hospitals/
        articles/faq-how-and-why-we-rank-and-rate-hospitals.

34   **cataract surgery, according to the Cleveland
        Clinic**   "Cole Eye Institute Outcomes,"
        Cleveland Clinic, accessed April 13, 2021, https://
        my.clevelandclinic.org/departments/eye/outcomes/693-
        cataract-surgery-complications.

36   **study related to surgery, conducted in North
      Carolina**   Frank A. Sloan, Christopher J. Conover, and
      Dawn Provenzale, "Hospital Credentialing and Quality
      of Care," *Social Science & Medicine*, January 2000, 50(1),
      77-88, https://www.sciencedirect.com/science/article/
      abs/pii/S0277953699002695.

39   **intermedullary nailing**   Matthew R. Bong,
      Kenneth J. Koval, and Kenneth A. Egol, "The History
      of Intramedullary Nailing," *Bulletin of the NYU Hospital for
      Joint Diseases*, 2006, 64(3 & 4), http://presentationgrafix.
      com/_dev/cake/files/archive/pdfs/581.pdf.

40   **revered mentor of a generation of surgeons**
      Ralph B. Blasier, "The Problem of the Aging Surgeon:
      When Surgeon Age Becomes a Surgical Risk Factor,"
      Clinical Orthopaedics and Related Research, February 2009,
      467(2), 402-411, https://www.ncbi.nlm.nih.gov/pmc/
      articles/PMC2628499/.

41   **develop new skills**   Ibid.

42   **when not to operate**   "Knowing When Not to
      Operate," *BMJ*, February 6, 1999, 318(7180), https://
      www.ncbi.nlm.nih.gov/pmc/articles/PMC1114811/.

43   **In Virginia, state legislators brokered a deal**
      Greg Weatherford, "'A Whole New Day': With Medicaid
      Expansion Lowering Costs, Health Systems Are Also
      Expanding," Virginia Business, September 2, 2019,
      https://www.virginiabusiness.com/article/a-whole-new-
      day/.

44   **Inova Health System**   Inova website, "Fairfax Medical Campus," accessed April 14, 2021, https://www.inova.org/locations/inova-fairfax-medical-campus.

44   **three-hundred-million-dollar upgrade**   Karen Graham, "Inova Loudoun to Open New \$300M Hospital Tower April 13," Loudoun Times-Mirror, April 8, 2020, https://www.loudountimes.com/news/inova-loudoun-to-open-new-300m-hospital-tower-april-13/article_ed9e83a6-790c-11ea-bb48-f3c3e081daa0.html.

44   **Carilion Clinic is forging ahead**   Luanne Rife, "Carilion Announces \$300M Expansion in Roanoke," Roanoke Times, May 15, 2019, https://roanoke.com/business/carilion-announces-300m-expansion-in-roanoke/article_fc495246-409f-53f3-8d7e-a480d10eb608.html.

44   **rescheduling surgeries from inpatient to outpatient facilities**   Joan Dentler, "Outpatient Migration: 6 Trends and Developments," Becker's Hospital Review, May 21, 2018, https://www.beckershospitalreview.com/hospital-management-administration/outpatient-migration-6-trends-and-developments.html.

45   **in thirty-five states**   "CON-Certificate of Need State Laws," National Conference of State Legislature website, December 1, 2019, https://www.ncsl.org/research/health/con-certificate-of-need-state-laws.aspx.

45   **certificate of need**   Mercatus Center, "How State Certificate-of-Need (CON) Laws Affect Access to Health Care," Medium, May 12, 2015, https://medium.com/concentrated-benefits/how-state-certificate-of-need-con-laws-impact-access-to-health-care-b8d3ec84242f.

46   **CONs have done just the opposite**   Ibid.

46   **in Virginia, freestanding ASCs**   Kate Masters, "Inside (Another) Failed Attempt to Reform Health Care Facility Approvals in Virginia," *Virginia Mercury*, March 10, 2020, https://www.virginiamercury. com/2020/03/10/behind-the-failed-efforts-to-make-2020-the-year-of-copn-reform-in-virginia/.

46   **in neighboring Maryland, ASCs are exempt**   Ibid.

46   **Medicare cost for outpatient cataract surgery at an HOPD**   Angie Stewart, "HOPD vs. ASCs: 5 Insights on the Reimbursement Gap," *ASC Review*, April 6, 2018, https://www.beckersasc.com/asc-coding-billing-and-collections/hopd-vs-ascs-5-insights-on-the-reimbursement-gap.html.

47   **infection rate at HOPD surgery centers** "Benchmarking Study of 1,000,000 Demonstrates Minimal Surgical Site Infections, Emergency Department Visits and Readmission Rates," *ASC Review*, August 24, 2017, https://www.beckersasc.com/asc-news/benchmarking-study-of-1-000-000-surgeries-in-ascs-demonstrates-minimal-surgical-site-infections-emergency-department-visits-and-readmission-rates.html.

47   **teaching hospitals have similar or less cost** Laura Joszt, "Teaching Hospitals Have Similar or Lower Cost of Care as Nonteaching Hospitals for Medicare Patients," *AJMC*, June 20, 2019, https://www.ajmc.com/view/teaching-hospitals-have-similar-or-lower-costs-of-care-as-nonteaching-hospitals-for-medicare-patients.

47   **generally accepted that academic medical centers cost more**   Sally Pobojewski, "Why Academic Medical Centers Cost More," *University Record*, December 14, 1998, https://ur.umich.edu/9899/Dec14_98/12.htm.

47   **indirect medical education (IME) payment**   "Indirect Medical Education (IME)," Centers for Medicare and Medicaid Services website, last modified August 4, 2014, https://www.cms.gov/Medicare/Medicare-Fee-for-Service-Payment/AcuteInpatientPPS/Indirect-Medical-Education-IME.

48   **uncompensated care totaled $39.1 billion**   "Uncompensatd Hospital Care Cost Fact Sheet," American Hospital Association, December 2010, https://www.aha.org/system/files/content/00-10/10uncompensatedcare.pdf.

48   **average nonprofit hospital spent a little more than 5 percent**   Andrew Krehbiel, "How Do Nonprofit Hospitals Deal with Charity Care? And Should We Care?" Health eCareers, December 20, 2017, https://www.healthecareers.com/article/healthcare-news/how-do-nonprofit-hospitals-deal-with-charity-care-and-should-we-care.

48   **median costs for four procedures**   Rachel Popa, "What 4 Outpatient Procedures Cost at ASCs vs. Hospitals, ASC Review, May 8, 2019," https://www.beckersasc.com/benchmarking/what-4-outpatient-procedures-cost-at-ascs-vs-hospitals.html.

49 **American Hospital Association, between 2009 and 2014**   Sara Heath, "How Do Healthcare Mergers and Acquisitions Impact Patients?" PatientEngagementHIT, August 7, 2018, https://patientengagementhit.com/news/how-do-healthcare-mergers-and-acquisitions-impact-patients.

49 **Out of all the malpractice lawsuits**   Judy Greenwald, "Most Medical Malpractice Claims Litigated, but Few Go to Trial: Study," Business Insurance, May 24, 2012, https://www.businessinsurance.com/article/20120524/NEWS07/120529939.

Chapter 4

55 **Hospital-based medical errors**   Johns Hopkins website, "Study Suggests Medical Errors Now Third Leading Cuse of Death in the U.S.," news release, May 3, 2016, Hop https://www.hopkinsmedicine.org/news/media/releases/study_suggests_medical_errors_now_third_leading_cause_of_death_in_the_us.

55 **250,000 to 440,000 deaths each year**   Ibid.

55 **There are errors of:**   John T. James, "A New, Evidence-Based Estimate of Patient Harms Associated with Hospital Care," *Journal of Patient Safety*, September 2013, 9(3), 122-128, https://journals.lww.com/journalpatientsafety/Fulltext/2013/09000/A_New,_Evidence_based_Estimate_of_Patient_Harms.2.aspx.

55   **Representative John Murtha**   Bradley Blackburn, "Medical Alerts: Murtha's Death a Surgical Mistake, and Second Report of Broken-Heart Syndrome," ABC News, February 9, 2010, https://abcnews.go.com/WN/john-murtha-death-surgical-mistake-medical-report-broken-heart-syndrome/story?id=9787211.

55   **beta blocker after heart surgery**   Mihai Gheorghiade, Wendy A. Gattis, and Christopher M. O'Connor, "Treatment Gaps in the Pharmacologic Management of Heart Failure," *Reviews in Cardiovascular Medicine*, 2002, 3 Supplement 3, https://pubmed.ncbi. nlm.nih.gov/12447157/.

55   **nineteen-year-old who experienced shortness of breath**   John James, *A Sea of Broken Hearts: Patient Rights in a Dangerous, Profit-Driven Health System*, Bloomington, IN: AuthorHouse, 2007, 14-46.

56   **Ten to 20 percent of patients**   "What Is Diagnostic Error?" Society to Improve Diagnosis in Medicine, accessed April 14, 2021, https://www.improvediagnosis. org/what-is-diagnostic-error/.

56   **they are where more deaths happen**   Stanford School of Medicine website, Palliative Care page, "Where Do Americans Die?" accessed April 14, 2021, https:// palliative.stanford.edu/home-hospice-home-care-of-the-dying-patient/where-do-americans-die/.

58   **study of 145,527 patients**   Andrew M. Ibrahim, Amir A. Ghafen, Jyothi R. Thumma, et al., "Variation in Outcomes at Bariatric Surgery Centers of Excellence, *JAMA Surgery*, July 2017, 152(7), 629-636, https://jamanetwork.com/journals/jamasurgery/fullarticle/2622647.

59   ***U.S. News & World Report* is the most famous** U.S. News & World Report website, Rankings and Advice page, accessed April 14, 2021, https://www.usnews.com/rankings.

59   **The magazine ranks hospitals**   U.S. News & World Report website, Hospital Rankings & Ratings page, accessed April 14, 2021, https://health.usnews.com/best-hospitals.

60   **Hospital Compare**   CMS.gov, Hospital Compare page, accessed April 14, 2021, https://www.cms.gov/Medicare/Quality-Initiatives-Patient-Assessment-Instruments/HospitalQualityInits/HospitalCompare.

61   **Vizient**   Vizient website, accessed April 14, 2021, https://www.vizientinc.com/what-we-do.

61   ***Fortune*/IBM Watson Health 100 Top Hospitals** Watson Health 100 Top Hospitals website, accessed April 14, 2021, https://www.ibm.com/watson-health/services/100-top-hospitals.

61   **The 100 Top Hospitals and 15 Top Health System** Fortune editors and IBM Watson Health, "Introducing the Fortune/IBM Watson Health 100 Top Hospitals," Fortune, June 30, 2020, https://fortune.com/2020/06/30/100-top-hospitals-2020-ibm-watson-health/.

61 **Medicare Provider Analysis and Review (MEDPAR)** CMS.gov, MEDPAR page, accessed April 14, 2021, https://www.cms.gov/Research-Statistics-Data-and-Systems/Statistics-Trends-and-Reports/MedicareFeeforSvcPartsAB/MEDPAR.

61 **Healthgrades** Healthgrades website, Hospital Ratings & Awards Methodologies page, accessed April 14, 2021, https://www.healthgrades.com/quality/ratings-awards/methodology.

62 **Leapfrog Group** The Leapfrog Group website, home page, accessed April 14, 2021, https://www.leapfroggroup.org/.

62 **Joint Council Quality Check** The Joint Commission website, "Quality Check and Quality Reports," accessed April 14, 2021, https://www.jointcommission.org/en/about-us/facts-about-the-joint-commission/quality-check-and-quality-reports/.

62 **Consumer Reports** "Is Your Hospital Really as Safe as You Think?" *Consumer Reports*, March 2014, https://www.consumerreports.org/cro/2014/03/is-your-hospital-really-as-safe-

63 **sources for all heart surgery data** STS National Database, Society of Thoracic Surgeons, accessed April 14, 2021, https://www.sts.org/registries/sts-national-database.

63 **Society of Thoracic Surgeons has developed** Ibid.

63 **Public reporting is available for three of the STS** Ibid.

Chapter 5

68 **Consumerism, according to the Institute for Healthcare Consumerism Forum** "How the Rise of Consumerism is Impacting Health Plans ... and How It Drives the Need for the Right Information at the Right Time," Healthedge website, accessed April 13, 2021, https://www.healthedge.com/sites/default/files/insights/2018_HE_WP_Consumerism.pdf.

69 **Free Market Medical Association** Free Market Medical Association website, accessed April 12, 2021, https://fmma.org.

86 **home exercises, mechanical cervical traction** Sherry Tsao and Peter Pidcoe, "The Management of a Patient with a Cervical Disc Herniation: A Case Report," *Clinical Medicine. Case Reports* vol. 1 45-9, May 22, 2008, https://www.ncbi.nlm.nih.gov/pmc/articles/PMC3785210/.

Chapter 6

100 **Institute of Medicine/National Academy of Medicine defines quality** Institute of Medicine (US) Committee on Quality of Health Care in America, *Crossing the Quality Chasm: A New Health System for the 21st Century*, Washington, DC: National Academies Press, 2001; PMID: 25057539, https://www.ncbi.nlm.nih.gov/books/NBK222265/.

100 **Agency for Healthcare Research and Quality**
Carolyn M. Clancy, MD, "Recognizing High-quality
Health Care," US Department of Health & Human
Services, October 16, 2007, https://archive.ahrq.
gov/news/columns/navigating-the-health-care-
system/101607.html.

100 **It further explains** Ibid.

100 **"The Strategy That Will Fix Healthcare,"**
Michael E. Porter and Thomas H. Lee, "The Strategy
That Will Fix Healthcare," Harvard Business Review,
October 2013, https://hbr.org/2013/10/the-strategy-
that-will-fix-health-care.

101 *keystone habits* Charles Duhigg, *The Power of Habit:
Why We Do What We Do in Life and Business*, New York:
Random House, 2012.

101 **proficiency in a specific procedure** Hari Nathan,
John L. Cameron, Michael A. Choti, et al., "The Volume-
Outcomes Effect in Hepato-Pancreato-Biliary Surgery:
Hospital versus Surgeon Contributions and Specificity of
the Relationship," *Journal of the American College of Surgeons*,
April 2009; 208(4):528-38, https://pubmed.ncbi.nlm.nih.
gov/19476786/.

101 **It may depend on how closely** Kyle H. Sheetz,
Usha Nullyalu, Hari Nathan, et al., "Association of
Surgeon Case Numbers of Pancreaticoduodenectomies
vs Related Procedures with Patient Outcomes to Inform
Volume-Based Credentialing," *Journal of the American
Medical Association*, April 29, 2020, https://jamanetwork.
com/journals/jamanetworkopen/fullarticle/2765071.

102   **Value is defined by Porter**   Michael E. Porter
        and Thomas H. Lee, "The Strategy That Will Fix
        Healthcare," Harvard Business Review, October 2013,
        https://hbr.org/2013/10/the-strategy-that-will-fix-
        health-care.

103   **Space Shuttle *Columbia***   Ben Paynter, "Close Calls
        Are Near Disasters, Not Lucky Breaks," Wired, August
        14, 2012, https://www.wired.com/2012/08/st-essay-
        close-calls/.

103   **Measures of quality can be categorized**   Chase
        Bennett, Grace Xiong, Serena Hu, et al., "What Is the
        State of Quality Measurement in Spine Surgery?" *Clinical
        Orthopaedics and Related Research, 476*(4), 725–731, https://
        www.ncbi.nlm.nih.gov/pmc/articles/PMC6260101/.

103   **AHRQ provides helpful resources**   Carolyn M.
        Clancy, MD, "Recognizing High-quality Health Care,"
        US Department of Health & Human Services, October
        16, 2007, https://archive.ahrq.gov/news/columns/
        navigating-the-health-care-system/101607.html.

105   **Reviews of the literature**   Chase Bennett, Grace
        Xiong, Serena Hu, et al., "What Is the State of Quality
        Measurement in Spine Surgery?" *Clinical Orthopaedics and
        Related Research, 476*(4), 725–731, https://www.ncbi.nlm.
        nih.gov/pmc/articles/PMC6260101/; B. J. sun, R. N.
        Kamal, G. K. Lee, and R. S. Nazerali, "Quality Measures
        in Ventral Hernia Repair: A Systematic Review," *Hernia*,
        December 2018, 22(6):1023-1032m https://pubmed.
        ncbi.nlm.nih.gov/29961197/; Robin N. Kamal, David
        Ring, Edward Akelman, et al., "Quality Measures
        in Upper Limb Surgery," *Journal of Bone and Joint*

Surgery, American volume, March 16, 2016, 98(6):505-10, https://pubmed.ncbi.nlm.nih.gov/26984919/; Rahim N. Nazerali, Micaela A. Finnegan, Vasu Divi, et al., "Quality Measures in Breast Reconstruction: A Systematic Review," *Annals of Plastic Surgery*, September 2017, 79(3):320-325, https://pubmed.ncbi.nlm.nih. gov/28570449/; Michael J. Rosen, "Quality Measures in Hernia Surgery," *Surgical Clinics of North America*, June 2018, 98(3):441-455, https://pubmed.ncbi.nlm.nih. gov/29754614/; Conroy Chow, Joyce T. Yuan, Emily S. Ruiz, et al., "Performance Measures in Dermatologic Surgery: A Review of the Literature and Future Directions," *Dermatologic Surgery*, June 2019, 45(6):836-843, https://pubmed.ncbi.nlm.nih.gov/31021903/.

105 **positive relationship between surgical volume** Johannes Morche, Tim Mathes, and Dawid Pieper, "Relationship between Surgeon Volume and Outcomes: A Systematic Review of Systematic Reviews," Systematic Reviews, November 29, 2016, 5(1), 204, https://www. ncbi.nlm.nih.gov/pmc/articles/PMC5129247/.

105 **considerable variation in surgical outcomes** Kyle H. Sheetz, Andrew M. Ibrahim, Hari Nathan, et al., "Variation in Surgical Outcomes across Networks of the Highest-Rated US Hospitals, *JAMA Surgery*, March 13, 2019, 154(6), 510-515, https://jamanetwork.com/ journals/jamasurgery/fullarticle/2727990.

105 **volume-outcome relationship** Hari Nathan, John L. Cameron, Michael A. Choti, et al., "The Volume-Outcomes Effect in Hepato-Pancreato-Biliary Surgery: Hospital versus Surgeon Contributions and Specificity of

the Relationship," *Journal of the American College of Surgeons*, April 2009; 208(4):528-38, https://pubmed.ncbi.nlm.nih. gov/19476786/.

105 **value in assessing surgeon volume** Kyle H. Sheetz, Usha Nullyalu, Hari Nathan, et al., "Association of Surgeon Case Numbers of Pancreaticoduodenectomies vs Related Procedures with Patient Outcomes to Inform Volume-Based Credentialing," *Journal of the American Medical Association*, April 29, 2020, https://jamanetwork. com/journals/jamanetworkopen/fullarticle/2765071; Bradley J. Needleman, Stacy A. Brethauer, and Timothy M. Pawlik, "Assessing a Surgeon's Competency for High-Risk Procedures: Should We Be Looking at the Bigger Picture?" *Journal of the American Medical Association*, April 29, 2020, https://jamanetwork.com/journals/ jamanetworkopen/fullarticle/2765067.

107 **Categories of patient-reported outcomes** David Cella, Elizabeth A. Hahn, Sally E. Jensen, et al., *Patient- Reported Outcomes in Performance Measurement*, Research Triangle Park (NC): RTI Press, 2015, https://www.ncbi. nlm.nih.gov/books/NBK424378/.

107 **surgeons are credentialed by individual hospitals** "Statement on Credentialing and Privileging and Volume Performance Issues," American College of Surgeons website, April 1, 2018, https://www.facs.org/about-acs/ statements/111-credentialing.

107 **Specialty societies may provide guidelines** J. Pearl, E. Fellinger, B. J. Dunkin, et al., "Guidelines for Privileging and Credentialing Physicians in Gastrointestinal Endoscopy," SAGES (Society of

American Gastrointestinal and Endoscopic Surgeons)
website, June 2016, https://www.sages.org/publications/
guidelines/guidelines-privileging-credentialing-physicians-
gastrointestinal-endoscopy/; Mitchell S. Cappell and
David M. Friedel, "Stricter National Standards Are
Required for Credentialing of Endoscopic-Retrograde-
Cholangiopancreatography in the United States," *World
Journal of Gastroenterology*, July 21, 2019, *25*(27):3468–
3483, https://www.ncbi.nlm.nih.gov/pmc/articles/
PMC6658394/.

108   **age alone is not a good discriminator**   E. Patchen
Dellinger, Carlos A. Pellegrini, and Thomas H. Gallagher,
"The Aging Physician and the Medical Profession: A
Review," *JAMA Surgery*, October 1, 2017, 152(10):967-
971, https://pubmed.ncbi.nlm.nih.gov/28724142/;
Robert T. Sataloff, Mary Hawkshaw, Joshua Kutinsky, and
Edward A. Maitz, "The Aging Physician and Surgeon,
Ear, Nose, & Throat Journal, April-May 2016, 95(4-5):E35-
48, https://pubmed.ncbi.nlm.nih.gov/27140028/.

108   **Review of surgical videos**   Constantinos Loukas,
"Video Content Analysis of Surgical Procedures,"
Surgical Endoscopy, February 2018, 32(2):553-568, https://
pubmed.ncbi.nlm.nih.gov/29075965/; Aashay Vaidya,
Abdullatif Aydin, Joanne Ridgley, et al., "Current Status
of Technical Skills Assessment Tools in Surgery: A
Systematic Review," *Journal of Surgical Research*, February
2020, 246:342-378, https://pubmed.ncbi.nlm.nih.
gov/31690531/.

108   **For example, mobilizing the gallbladder neck**
L. S. G. L. Wauben, W. M. U. van Grevenstein, R. H.
M. Goossens, et al., "Operative Notes Do Not Reflect

Reality in Laparoscopic Cholecystectomy," *British Journal of Surgery*, October 2011, 98(10):1431-6, https://pubmed.ncbi.nlm.nih.gov/21633952/.

Chapter 7

113 **review of a large national malpractice carrier's claim data**   Anupam B. Jena, Seth Seabury, Darius Lakdawalla, and Amitabh Chandra, "Malpractice Risk According to Physician Specialty," *New England Journal of Medicine*, August 18, 2011, 365(7): 629–636, https://www.nejm.org/doi/full/10.1056/nejmsa1012370.

114 **Council for Affordable Quality Healthcare** CAQH website, "About CAQH" page, accessed April 12, 2021, https://www.caqh.org/about/about-caqh.

114 **National Practitioner Data Bank**   NPDB website, "About Us" page, accessed April 12, 2021, https://www.npdb.hrsa.gov/topNavigation/aboutUs.jsp.

115 **One study in 2003 did find "consistent differences** T. M. Waters, F. V. Lefevre, and P. P. Budetti, "Medical School Attended as a Predictor of Medical Malpractice Claims," *Quality and Safety in Health Care*, October 2003, 12:330–336, https://www.researchgate.net/publication/9061253_Medical_school_attended_as_a_predictor_of_medical_malpractice_claims.

ABOUT THE AUTHOR
AND CONTRIBUTORS

Author
Sanjay Prasad

Sanjay Prasad, MD, FACS, has been a practicing surgeon for nearly thirty years in the super-specialized field of otology, neurotology, and skull base surgery, a subspecialty within otolaryngology head and neck surgery (ENT). Prasad is one of the few surgeons in his specialty to complete three fellowships in neurotology, advanced head and neck oncologic surgery, and cranial base surgery. He is an assistant professor at George Washington University. As a medical director for an ambulatory surgery center, he was one of the first to start bundling surgical services for all-inclusive prices in 2014.

In the same year, Prasad founded SurgiPrice, Inc. with subsidiaries SurgiQuality and SurgiConnect, with a mission to help surgical patients connect to best-in-class surgeons who operate in a cost-efficient environment.

Prasad practices and lives in the Washington, DC, area with his amazing wife, Deepika, and their four very accomplished adult children, Meghna, Kiran, Neha, and Dilan.

Contributors

Erin McKean

Erin McKean, MD, MBA, FACS, is the assistant dean for Student Services at the University of Michigan Medical School, associate chair for Clinical Operations in the Department of Otolaryngology–Head and Neck Surgery at Michigan Medicine, director of the Cranial Base Surgery Program, and an adjunct associate professor of neurosurgery.

Lauren Pritchard

Lauren Pritchard is originally from Charlotte, North Carolina. She has six years of experience in healthcare and currently serves as the information security officer for SurgiPrice, Inc. and concierge advocate for SurgiQuality. She is also a medical assistant for a private ENT practice.

Pritchard earned her bachelor's degree in exercise and sport science with a minor in chemistry from the University of North Carolina at Chapel Hill. Currently, she is pursuing a dual master's degree in health administration and business at Pfeiffer University. In her free time, she enjoys spending time with her husband and golden retriever, traveling, and cheering on the Carolina Panthers or Tarheels.

Sapan Shah

Sapan Shah, MD, JD, is the managing partner of Alera Group's HPL Division and a board director of Alera Group, a national insurance and financial services firm. Sapan joined Alera in 2017 when Alera acquired Flagship Healthcare, which he co-founded in 2008. Being a physician and an attorney, Sapan has a unique perspective on medical professional liability issues and innovative business strategies in healthcare.

An active angel investor in Hyde Park Angels (HPA) in Chicago, Sapan has invested in more than forty startups. He is also on the board of directors of Kaizen Health, a board observer for Blueprint, and was a board director for Regroup Therapy, all HPA healthcare portfolio companies.

Sapan is admitted to the Illinois Bar and is on the board of advisors for the Burke Neurological Institute in White Plains, New York. Sapan lives in Libertyville, Illinois, with his wife, Rachna Shah, MD, an allergist in private practice.

Carl H. Snyderman

Carl H. Snyderman, MD, MBA, FACS, is professor of otolaryngology and neurological surgery at the University of Pittsburgh School of Medicine, and otolaryngology director of the Center for Cranial Base Surgery at the University of Pittsburgh Medical Center. Snyderman also serves as vice chair of Quality and Safety for the Department of Otolaryngology at the University of Pittsburgh Medical Center.

Learn More about SurgiQuality and Share Your Surgical Journey

Visit SurgiQuality.com to discover more about how patients are taking unparalleled control over the most important decisions they'll ever make.

To read about experiences from people like you, go to PatientStorybook.com. There, you'll find personal accounts of patients who have undergone unnecessary procedures, misdiagnoses, and surgical complications. You'll learn how SurgiQuality has helped them overcome medical adversity. Once registered at PatientStorybook.com, you can also add your story, and you'll receive SurgiQuality's free quarterly newsletter.

Made in the USA
Middletown, DE
21 June 2021